THE
SAVAGE
DISCIPLINE

THE
SAVAGE
DISCIPLINE

JESSE TRAVIS SCOTT

Matador
Unit E2 Airfield Business Park,
Harrison Road, Market Harborough,
Leicestershire. LE16 7UL
Tel: 0116 2792299
Email: books@troubador.co.uk
Web: www.troubador.co.uk/matador
Twitter: @matadorbooks

ISBN 978 1803137 100

British Library Cataloguing in Publication Data.
A catalogue record for this book is available from the British Library.

Printed and bound in Great Britain by 4edge Limited
Typeset in 10pt Effra by Troubador Publishing Ltd, Leicester, UK

Matador is an imprint of Troubador Publishing Ltd

To all the trials and tribulations, wins, losses, and draws (you know who you are) – We can always do better, improve, learn from our mistakes, and persevere.

CONTENTS

"The struggle is great, the task divine – to gain mastery, freedom, happiness, and tranquility."

- EPICTETUS

Thank you for purchasing, and (hopefully) reading this book, a culmination of decades of learning and study, using myself as a guinea pig in determining what works and what doesn't. My reasons for writing this book are simple, to share my knowledge and learnings. Seeing as we're all stardust partaking in this ultimate human experience, what works for me might just work for you or someone else too. If not, that's valuable too, as now you know what not to do! The sharing of knowledge and experience is one of our primary human responsibilities, passing on what we know in the hope others can learn and build upon it along the way.

The methods herein have helped me to achieve a successful and healthy lifestyle. I was born to a working middle-class family in a small Canadian city, not part of the one-percent, but luckier than most and given plenty of advantages to work with. I didn't complete high school or university but didn't let that hold me back – as you'll come to see in this book, I'm not a big believer in excuses.

In the ensuing years I have held half a dozen positions at NATO (the North Atlantic Treaty Organisation www.nato.int), receiving numerous medals and commendations, while climbing through four civilian ranks in an eighteen month span. Post-NATO, I held senior leadership roles at two global Fortune 500 companies with annual revenues in excess of $25 billion. In between, I've been lucky enough to join two startups who achieved the lauded 'unicorn' status, with valuations exceeding $1 billion before being publicly listed on the stock market. I play multiple instruments, have written hundreds of poems, songs, two novels and numerous short stories to date. I train my body 4-6 days per week and despite having crossed into the over-forty threshold, I can keep up with, and outdo most in the so-called prime of life twenties.

This concept and framework for this book came to me in a 45-minute blast just after 5am on a Monday morning, as I lay in awake in bed collecting my thoughts. I jotted down twenty-some chapter ideas with point form notes against them. When I reflected on my thoughts a little later in the day, I gave myself a deadline and committed to completing a first draft of the book-to-be in sixty days. I hit that target, and the book you're reading is the result of those efforts.

Throughout my life I'd always fantasized about having a mentor or guru of some sort. In my mind, this guru was a wise old individual, experienced in the ways and wiles of life to help guide my decisions and choices. A Doc Emmett Brown to my Marty McFly. In hindsight I suppose I was looking for a form of assurance and a backup, perhaps even someone I could blame when things went wrong. I suspect this is something or someone everyone longs for – a form of guidance to ensure they're making the right choices for themselves personally and the world at large. The reality is no single individual could guide you in such a manner because no matter how alike we all are, being built from the same stuff, we're all inherently different. Through the course of our learnings and experiences in life, along with the choices we make, we become ever more unique. We're an amalgamation of those base genetics and experiences which no one has had previously and no one will again.

So, what can we do to help ensure we make the right choices? We can approach life not only with a childlike curiosity and experimental mindset but also with the right amount of self-discipline to learn from our mistakes and continue to improve, fostering good habits and ridding ourselves of the bad as we make our own journeys through life. Such a life will involve many phases, some good, some bad, some easy, some hard, and numerous mentors and individuals you'll learn from – both living and deceased. From these we take pieces of knowledge here, bits of inspiration there, all the while gaining wisdom and experience to approach and deal with the situations that confront us a little better each time.

"It is not the most intellectual of the species that survives; it is not the strongest that survives, but the species that survives is the one that is able best to adapt and adjust to the changing environment in which it finds itself." – Charles Darwin, Origin of Species (1859)

The pages that follow contain knowledge and insights accumulated over years of living, trial and error, scraping away and finding bits and pieces of information and nuggets of wisdom along the way. Not every single thing will work for everyone, and many won't work forever. The one all-encompassing facet I hope to impart within these texts is that **adaptability and dynamism are key**. There's a significant difference between knowing vs. trusting vs. believing – you need to find what works for you at any given time, but not make it dogma.

Reassess, reevaluate and keep pushing and pulling and switching things up. Keep your mind and body guessing, learning, renewing, and fresh – make it fun and challenge yourself. Never be afraid to change your mind or style of doing something. Despite the claims politicians love to hurl at their opponents, changing one's mind or opinion does not make them a hypocrite or wishy-washy, it signifies learning and growth.

This book collects and harnesses strategies and tactics humanity throughout the ages has bequeathed from parent to child, elder to initiate, and teacher to student. Choice aspects harvested and distilled into easy to understand principles which can be applied to modern living, enabling optimization of the mind and body, assisting you in navigating both the challenges and pleasures experienced throughout your life journey.

The title, **The Savage Discipline**, is significant in that the bulk of these principles are inherent to the human experience, naturally complementing how our biochemistry and psychology are designed and have evolved. In that sense, it is savage, raw, or wild. Similar to the grasses and plants that will inevitably poke their way through modern buildings and concrete, this is our nature and it will eventually triumph. Savage has a dual meaning – it can be viewed as something completely free, unleashed or untethered but also a derogatory term for cultures and ways which we neglected to understand. In that throwing away valuable learning opportunities, ancient, forgotten, and misunderstood methods. Methods which are dynamic and powerful, enabling us not only to survive but to thrive and circumvent obstacles.

The "noble savage" concept fits here. Many of the methods and concepts in this book aim to restore and align the mind and body with ways that were once automatic, ingrained, and natural, but due to the ever-increasing complexity of modern life have become neglected or forgotten.

The word "Discipline" may at first seem contrary to that which is savage or wild. Still, when you consider how much our lives and society have deviated from the world in which we evolved to thrive, along with the distractions and obstacles we unwittingly put in the way of our optimal selves, you'll see where the discipline aspect comes into play. We require discipline, diligence, strength, and courage of conviction to keep ourselves not just healthy, but at our best.

Should you choose to follow some of the methods detailed in this book, I ask you to be prepared to make an effort; the path to change and growth isn't often an easy one. The Internet and media are awash with many gentle messages of understanding, espousing the benefits of self-love, being easy on yourself, and giving yourself a break. I'm not trying to take away from these – they're important, and there is a time and place for them. But there's also a time and place for self-discipline, hard work, effort, and diligence. Depending on you as an individual, I suspect the concepts and methods in this book will lean more towards the latter end of the spectrum. By not working diligently and striving to be the best version of yourself, the only person you're cheating is yourself.

CHAPTER ONE

MORNING

Everyone has some kind of morning routine, even if it consists of being jarred awake by an alarm, smashing the snooze button three or four times, making a mad dash to the shower, running out the door and grabbing a takeout coffee somewhere along a rushed commute to the office. A morning like that makes my head spin, yet that's how it goes for many of us.

The worst part about the morning described above is that you've gotten your day off to a terrible start. It's like a sprinter having her feet misaligned in the starting block, not hearing the starting gun, *and* having a shoelace come untied yet still recovering and winning the race. Sure, it could happen, but the odds are against you and you're definitely not setting yourself up to win. The morning is where your day starts, and developing a method that puts you at your best is one of the first things you should do. Once you've got your routine down everything else will seem that much easier and take a little less effort. You'll start the day in control and you can focus the increased confidence and energy on other neglected aspects of your day and life.

Like the other concepts in this book, there's no one size fits all. What works for you now might not work as circumstances change and you grow. You need to be dynamic, open, and always questioning and honestly assessing what's working for you and what isn't.

Morning routines are a dime a dozen nowadays, every fitness guru, social media influencer, and business titan have their own methods which you can study. If you're the type who reads these, there may be some overlap; but hopefully, you'll get some new ideas too. If not and you've got this, already being a certified morning routine maestro, feel free to skip this chapter and move on to another – the book is made to work for and with you, not to bend you to its will.

Elements of my morning routine are outlined below, some are optional and I've marked them as such, but others are core aspects of a healthy start to your day. Following them gives you a solid foundation ensuring you're at your best when tackling whatever challenges may be thrown at you throughout the day. The concepts are listed in the order in which I apply them, but feel free to adjust and rearrange as you see fit.

THE WAKE-UP

Easy right? Everyone wakes up, and if you don't, then you've got more pressing concerns and should put this book down right now and go see a doctor. It amazes me how much difficulty so many people have in waking up, the alarm clock and snooze button scenario described at the beginning of the chapter makes my skin crawl. I cannot imagine a worse start to my day.

I'm going to generate some controversy right away, when I tell you to **Stop Using an Alarm**, at least most of the time. If you're traveling through multiple time zones and your body clock is out-of-sync, sure, there may be necessary reasons for an alarm. But it should serve as an emergency back-up, not something to be relied upon to wake you up. If the latter is the case then there is something wrong with the sleep you are getting, as your body and mind are not rested enough for you to wake. To resolve this you'll have to make some adjustments to other parts of your life, common culprits being caffeine intake, stress, anxiety, exercise, the time you go to bed, and alcohol consumption – more on these later.

Let's do a quick test – look away from this book and any potential screens or clocks and guess the time right now, this very minute, down to the minute. I'm willing to bet you were within 30 minutes of the actual time, probably less. I find I'm usually within 5-10 minutes. This is because your mind and body know what time it is. We've evolved to function on the 24-hour cycle of the Earth's rotation. Thousands of years of human history have encoded the rhythm of the day into our bodies and minds. Just how long do you think alarm clocks have been around, anyways? We survived before them and we can survive without them.

Ever notice how you tend to wake up at about the same time on weekends or holidays when you don't have to get up for anything specific, even without an alarm? That's because your body and mind are trained and accustomed to waking at that time – you do not need to be jolted awake by some shrill and piercing noise throwing off your equilibrium and giving you a kick in the pants to start the day. Have some faith in yourself and give this a try – if you're nervous, start with weekends or days when you don't have a strict schedule. Next, try setting your alarm back a little later than usual, e.g., if you usually set it for 07:00, set it for 07:10 and see if you don't wake up at 07:00 regardless.

MINUTE POST WAKE-UP

Don't open your eyes upon first waking up, try not to – sight is a powerful and overwhelming sense but it's also the easiest to turn off. Our other senses are already coming online and will be providing data and input to the brain. I find it useful to delay the onslaught of vision and take a few minutes to focus on the raw and natural thoughts in my mind, keeping them as undisturbed as possible – recall dreams you had overnight, strange ideas, reflections on something you did or want to do, etc. I find many of my best and most exciting ideas come at this time of day.

When you do open your eyes, **don't reach for your phone or device** – if you feel the need to check the time, go ahead. Just don't read those alerts, emails, or texts, there's plenty of time for that later in the day. If they waited for the 6-8 hours you (hopefully) slept, they can hold out for another 30 minutes or so. Instead, breathe, relax, stretch, let your mind and body adjust to being awake.

[Optional] I always have a book of poetry or philosophy on the go (more on that in the Reading chapter), sitting within easy reach on my bedside table. The first thing I do every morning after opening my eyes is to prop myself up and **read a few lines, poems, or pages**.

It can be as little as a four-line poem or on days when I'm drawn into something and want to have a leisurely wake-up, I'll go through twenty pages or more. I love the idea of seeding my mind with a few foreign concepts, feelings, insights or wisdom right after it's woke to grease the wheels and add new twists to thoughts and ideas of my own.

Make your bed. This takes all of a minute to do, maybe two if you tossed and turned a lot, or five if you want to do a hotel or hospital-style job. If someone else is sharing your bed, I think a fair rule is that the last one out of bed makes the bed!

Brush & Floss Your Teeth. Yes, your mother and dentist were right, and anyone you may be lucky enough to kiss throughout the day will appreciate your good oral hygiene.

The real benefit of these last two points are that no matter how much your day seems to go off the rails, when you inevitably collapse into your bed at night, you'll know that you got that right; it went off without a hitch – you've got a comfy and perfectly made bed waiting for you, and your teeth and mouth feel great.

HYDRATE

Drink some water. Still or sparkling, doesn't matter – but water, not something with added sugars and not soda, diet or zero or whatever masquerade it throws up on its label. If you want to add some spice and flavor to your water, try infusing it with fruits or herbs such as lemon and mint. I add a small amount of natural salts (sea or Himalayan, etc.) to help your body absorb the water and replenish some minerals and electrolytes lost overnight.

Approximately 60% of our bodies are water with more significant quantities making up the composition of the brain, heart, and lungs. We feel the ill effects of dehydration much earlier than those of starvation. Studies show up to 75% of us are under-hydrated, and drinking too much water won't hurt as you urinate any excess out. The only time I don't like to drink too much water is when undertaking high-exertion exercise due to the uncomfortable feeling of it splashing around in my belly when I'm lifting, jumping, lunging, and twisting.

VITAMINS

This is a highly personalized part of your day. To determine the best combination for you, I'd recommend speaking to trained experts such as physicians, registered dieticians, nutritionists, or naturopaths. I consider myself a healthy individual (and medical examinations back this up) and have been blessed with no persistent ailments, allergies, or deficiencies to date. As such my daily vitamin intake is minimal, consisting of three pills and a little spritz of a spray in my mouth. The four basics I use are:

Multivitamin

The catch-all – Do your research and get a good quality brand. I prefer brands that are as natural and unprocessed as possible, primarily composed of organic ingredients. The reason we take multivitamins is to replace all the vitamins and minerals we aren't getting, most of which we used to get via our natural lives and diets. As human civilization spread beyond the plains of Africa and equatorial regions we had to find new ways to cope with our environmental conditions and to exist. The human body is very adaptable and can survive harsh treatment and conditions, but to thrive we need to ensure we give it the essential vitamins, minerals, and nutrients it needs.

BCAAs (Branch-Chained Amino Acids)

Amino acids are the building blocks of proteins, which comprise a large part of the human body. Certain amino acids are marked as essential, meaning the human body cannot generate them and they must be obtained through your diet. Found naturally in certain foods such as meats, eggs, and dairy products, or via BCAA supplements, they contain three key essential amino acids – leucine, isoleucine, and valine.

Depending on a variety of factors such as age, gender, and fitness level, between 25-40% of the human body is muscle and those three amino acids are scientifically proven to promote muscle growth, decrease muscle soreness, reduce exercise fatigue, and prevent muscle breakdown. This isn't just for athletes or bodybuilders – muscles are engaged in everything we do from our heart beating, to sitting down and standing up, to walking. We must take care of our muscles to ensure maximum efficiency and minimal fatigue.

Krill or Fish Oil

Both of these supplements provide Omega-3 fatty acids of the DHA (docosahexaenoic acid) and EPA (eicosatetraenoic acid) varieties. This ensures you're getting a good dose of healthy fats in the morning – the stuff that your brain runs on and energy comes from. Studies also show cardiovascular (heart) benefits from the consumption of krill and fish oils including reduced risk of heart attacks and coronary artery disease. Other potential benefits from taking krill or fish oil include reduced inflammation (various inflammations are the cause of many common ailments), reduction in joint pain (arthritis), dry eye relief, and reduction in premenstrual syndrome or tension (PMS / PMT) in women.

The main difference between the two is in their sources. Fish oil coming from oily fish (e.g., Sardines, Herring, etc.), whereas krill oil comes from krill – tiny shrimp-like crustaceans that sit near the bottom of the food chain, a favourite food of whales, seals, penguins and the like. I prefer krill oil as it tends to be sourced from less polluted Antarctic waters and the tiny krill are unlikely to be contaminated with heavy metals such as mercury or lead.

Vitamin D with K2

Depending on where you live and other demographic factors, studies suggest vitamin D deficiency affects between 20-60% of the population. Putting it right beside Iron as the top deficiencies found in individuals living in the western world. This harkens back to the origin of the human species, in that we evolved living outdoors along the equator and getting lots of sunlight, but as civilization progressed many of us have since migrated away, spending most of our time indoors.

Vitamin D, aka the "Sunshine Vitamin," is essential in that it helps our body absorb both calcium and phosphorus leading to strong and healthy bones and teeth, strengthening the immune system and helping stave off depression.

You'll often find vitamin D combined with vitamin K2, which activates a protein known as osteocalcin, responsible for integrating calcium into your bones. In a nutshell, K2 helps the vitamin D along in that job, ensuring maximum efficiency.

As mentioned above, I take my Vitamin D w/ K2 combo as a spray, but like the other vitamins, it's readily available in a variety of formats to suit your preference.

SHINE A LIGHT

There's nothing better to help wake you up and get your mind and body going than natural sunlight, which follows nicely after the piece on vitamin D (naturally found in sunlight). If you're able, one of the first things you should do in the morning is to **get some sunlight**. Preferably outside on your porch, balcony, or in your backyard if you've got access to either – otherwise a room with lots of windows will do. Sunlight helps reset your body clock and wake you up, not unlike a bear crawling out of its cave after a long winter hibernation, reemerging and stretching in the light of spring.

Depending on where you live this ritual may be tricky during the winter months when darkness rules and the sun may not rise until late in the day. In this case, I still recommend getting a few breaths of fresh outside air if at all possible. If not, there are alternatives on the market such as 'natural' light-emitting devices and bulbs, even some products which claim to emit natural light into other areas (such as the ears). I cannot speak to the efficacy of such things – I'll leave it to you should you wish to experiment and determine if it helps you.

MOVE

A key element of The Savage Discipline is the interconnection of body and mind – both need to be taken care of and trained for an individual to truly be at their best. This is your opportunity to **get some blood flowing to both your brain and body**. This isn't a full-blown workout or something requiring a large investment of time, rather a few minute's activity to help you feel awake and alive. Do a few squats, jumping jacks, push-ups, or hold a plank for a minute or ten.

MEDITATE

There's no big secret here – the word is out that meditation is good for everyone and it's something we all can and should do, regardless of age, gender, or locality. It puts things in perspective, reduces stress and anxiety, and trains your mind to accept yourself and the world around you. Despite its Eastern roots, I connect with meditation via Stoic philosophy. I've tried several methods of meditation including silent Vipassana retreats, and each and every experience has proven valuable in some way.

So many people have told me they're no good at meditation and can't do it – to this, I say it's important to remember that meditation is a practice, not something you're 'good' or 'bad' at, some days may feel and flow better than others but that's the nature of the beast and life itself. What is important is that you do practice and keep at it, providing consistency and ritual will only deepen and broaden your understanding and perspective. "Meditation ruined my day," said no one, ever.

Again, you don't have to be a monk or a Zen master of any kind to do this – but consistency, along with some effort and discipline is key. You should **practice some form of meditation daily**, even for 5-10 minutes. I prefer mornings as this is the traditional time, but whatever works for you and wherever you can fit it in is fine. There are many great apps to help with meditation nowadays, including Headspace, Calm, and others. There's also an infinite amount of free meditations available on YouTube. Play around with it, find something you like that works for you.

PHILOSOPHY [OPTIONAL]

This is me baring my soul and letting you in on one of my more unusual habits to poke fun as you wish. Every morning, after finishing my meditation, I'll read a passage or two of philosophy and aphorisms while holding a plank. As ridiculous as it sounds (and looks, as my wife will agree), it gives me some concepts and ideas to mull over while re-awakening my body muscles post-meditation. You could easily skip the plank and just read 1-2 aphorisms from a philosopher, theologian, or something else you're interested in.

WRITE, JOURNAL, SCRIBBLE, OR SCRATCH

This is so important to me, and I can't imagine a reason why someone wouldn't want to do this. Regardless of what you end up writing (and interspersing doodles and sketches therein is a great practice too), it's a fantastic feeling to have some form of long and winding record of your life throughout the years – and if that doesn't appeal to you, you can also make a ritual of destroying the writings periodically, it's all up to you.

You don't need to write War & Peace, and no one ever needs to see what you write, but **sit down and write**, let whatever it is that wants to come out flow, as beautiful or ugly as it may seem or feel at the time. You can have a method or plan of what you write every time (e.g., How you're feeling, about your day, priorities, things to do, hopes, dreams, desires, gratitudes, etc.), or you can simply do as I do and go with the flow. Some days I'll be an angsty teenager complaining about life and the universe. Others, I'll sketch out several fully formed business or story ideas. Sometimes I'll actually write a story or a poem or describe a dream. Most of the time, it's a combination of all of the above.

I do a page every morning with a cup of coffee by my side – you could do a sentence, a paragraph or five pages, again it's up to you, but write *something*.

SHOWER [OPTIONAL]

Chances are you already do this, I prefer to wait until after I exercise, but whenever you do it try making it cold, as cold as the water can go. I know it sounds awful but you'll be surprised how quickly your body acclimatizes to the cold water (which isn't actually that cold out of your household tap anyways). It's guaranteed to help wake both mind and body and get the circulation flowing and skin feeling great. If it happens to be a cold or wet day outside, you'll be less inclined to notice or be bothered by it when you step out.

SUMMARY

Think of your morning routine as your preparation, the constant pre-training to set you up for success throughout the day. No matter how cranky or offbeat I wake up, I force myself through the morning schedule above, each and every day, one-hundred percent of the time regardless of where I happen to be, and I can tell you without a doubt it makes me feel so much better for it. Not only does it help you to feel better immediately, on the off chance you woke up on the wrong side of the bed or not feeling your best, but it also gives you something to be proud of. A sense of accomplishment in knowing that despite any rough starts or curveballs life may throw your way, you've got this, you're in control, and you're going to succeed and make it work.

CHAPTER TWO

DIET & NUTRITION

Eating and drinking make up a substantial part of our day, fueling and hydrating the mind and body, and for pleasure – be it the social aspects or just digging into some grub you really love. Our overall health and fitness rest on a three-legged stool and as everyone knows, a two-legged stool will not stand up, it'll topple over, each leg essential and necessary for it to function.

This section isn't intended to help you lose or gain weight, instead focusing on optimal nutrition and diet for the human body. My waist size hasn't changed since I was 18 years old. You could put this down to genetics, exercise regimen, or diet, but in reality, it's probably a combination of all three. This section can be summarized into the following seven points:

- **Eat high quality, healthy, fats and proteins**. Make these the foundational core of your nutrition. Get them as wild, unprocessed, raw (in the case of dairy), and as natural as possible, preferably organic and free of added hormones or antibiotics.

- **Eat your fruit**. When our hunter-gather ancestors ere unable to make a kill or catch a fish, they often turned to the trees and bushes around them. Fruit don't always have to be sweet. Remember, avocados, olives, and all forms of squash (e.g., butternut, acorn, zucchini etc.) are fruits too. Organic is important here, but if that's not possible invest in a proper method to clean the sprays and pesticides from them. Fruits are preferable whole and not as a juice, gaining the benefit of the fiber. Juice alone is mostly fruit sugars.

- **Eat vegetables, but make sure they feel right for you.** Vegetables have their place and are full of a variety of essential nutrients and minerals, but it's helpful to take note of how they affect your body. Due to genetic makeup or other factors, certain vegetables may not sit well with everyone (e.g., those containing high amounts of sulphur etc.).

- **Eat wholegrains, but not too much** of them. Avoid processed and refined grains.

- **Drink mostly water, coffee or tea, au naturel and without sweeteners** – if you must have a sweeter, use something natural like raw honey or maple syrup, and again not too much. Don't drink soda of any kind, diet, zero, or whatever.

- **Don't overeat**. You don't need to eat three meals a day, or to have breakfast despite marketing claims and long out-of-date papers to the contrary. Eat when you're hungry and no more. Humans have been intermittently fasting as a necessity a lot longer than they've rolled out of bed to grab a bowl of cereal or a smoothie.

- **Added and refined sugars or carbs should be viewed as treats**. Not mainstays of every meal, every day.

FOOD AS FUEL

Most of humanity have come to accept evolution as fact – in that organisms change and adapt to their environment to better facilitate survival over time. Where issues arise is that 'over time' part, which is a geological blink of an eye, or a cosmological nano-instant, but takes thousands of human generations to occur. This is why our minds and brains still function best when consuming foods and nutrients similar to those we did during the dawning of our species.

PROTEINS

In recent years protein has become a bit of a marketing term – all sorts of treats and candy bars in the supermarket aisle boast of x grams of protein per serving. Why though? What's the big deal with protein, and why do we need it? The simple answer is that **protein is an essential building block for every cell in your body**, not only muscles, as it's often associated with bodybuilding or athletes. Yes, it provides a huge benefit for your musculature, including growth, strength, and recovery, but beyond that, it's necessary to build and repair the tissues in your organs, skin, bones, hair, nails, teeth – everything! Protein also helps with the immune system, blood clotting, vision, and hormones.

Protein is readily available if you consume animal products such as meat, fish, eggs, or dairy. You'll get all the essential amino acids and in the correct ratios, which stands to reason as animal tissues are very similar to human tissues. If you don't consume animal products those proteins and amino acids are still available, but you have to get a little more creative. Protein supplements such as powders, shakes, and bars are really only necessary for bodybuilders, athletes or individuals doing extreme forms of training or physical activity. They're often loaded with extraneous sugars and chemicals, so if you do use these, I'd recommend doing your research and paying for a quality brand made without refined sugars and using organic or grass-fed ingredients.

There are different estimates as to how much protein an individual needs, and this varies based on a number of factors such as age, gender, and activity level. As a general guideline it's good to aim for at least 1 gram per kilogram of weight per day (or .5 grams per pound).

Despite all the benefits of protein the average western diet has a major problem in this regard, that being: **Much of the meat, eggs, and dairy we eat is of poor quality.**

There's a simple and logical approach to all of this, – **Eat high quality meat, eggs, and dairy**. What does a subjective term such as 'high quality' mean in this case? Read on.

Most humans eat meat. We've done so from our earliest origins to the present day. I love meat, despite being a strict (and unhealthy) vegetarian for nine years of my life. The problem with a lot of meat-eating in our society is not just with the amount we eat but the quality and sourcing of the meat. For 99% of human history we ate natural, wild meats that we hunted, trapped, or fished, and it's unlikely we were lucky enough to catch something every day. In the present day we saunter down to the supermarket or a fast food joint, spend a dollar and get something claiming to be meat yet so far removed from the method and product mentioned above that it might as well be another classification or category of food altogether.

The majority of mass-marketed, factory-farmed meat is manufactured (I hesitate to use the word "grown") for maximum profit; in essence, this means generating the largest amount of meat possible in the least amount of space and time. To do so, animals that would normally take months or weeks to mature to slaughtering size are instead bulked-up and fed foods they wouldn't normally eat, helped along by shots, hormones, and who knows what to speed the process along. Similar to super-sizing your fast food meal, this results in Frankenstein-like monstrosities that grow much larger and faster than they would in their natural habitat. You've likely heard the expression, "You are what you eat." In recent years, research has shown this expression should have another word appended to more accurately reflect its nutritional value – "**You are what you eat eats.**" That's right, if you consume an animal that had been reared on unhealthy, unnatural foods, hormones, and the like, the trickle-down effect is loading all of those toxins straight into you, polluting your mind and body.

So, what does this all mean – that you should only eat wild meats and fish? Yes, for the most part, with some caveats – not all farms are created equal and not all farms practice the 'techniques' mentioned above. There are plenty of farms, often smaller, boutique, family-run establishments that raise livestock using old tried and trusted methods. It's slower and more expensive and that extra cost is passed onto the consumer – but wouldn't you rather support a small local business that's providing you with natural, healthy food of traceable origin, while eating less of it to offset the additional cost?

Do your research, speak to your local butchers, fishmongers, cheesemongers, and supermarkets. Look for labels such as "grass-fed" or "pastured" on your meats. Seek our pasture-raised eggs (better than cage free or free range), and raw (nonpasturized) dairy. When looking for new clothing, electronics, or a gym, we inform ourselves of the options, why would we do any less with something we're putting into our bodies and directly affecting our health?

FATS

Far and away the most maligned of essential nutrients fats have gotten a bad rap for decades. However in recent years due to updated, modern research and perhaps some diets which I won't bother mentioning, people have started seeing them in a new light.

Fats store and provide energy, as well as enabling the absorption of fat-soluble vitamins. Long thought to be a major cause of coronary diseases, that research has since been overturned. Many diets traditionally high in fat content (Mediterranean, French, Inuit) have a much lower occurrence rate of this type of disease than those who ate less fat but more processed and refined products with added sugars.

Fats can be broken down into the four broad categories, three of which we deem to be healthy or 'Good' fats, and the remaining being the unhealthy 'Bad' fats, to be avoided.

The Good – Monounsaturated, Polyunsaturated, and Saturated Fats

Healthy fats help fill you up and make you feel satiated, reducing the amount of food you need to eat overall, lowering calorie consumption and making you eat less. They are *good* for your heart and the health of your body, reducing the risk of stroke and lowering blood pressure.

Saturated fats are good for you too, but unlike monounsaturated and polyunsaturated, you should consume them in moderation. Easily to identifiable as the fats that are are solid at room temperature but render to a liquid when heated. They're also some of the most delicious fats.

Good Fat Sources

Monounsaturated	Olive Oil, Avocados (and Avocado oil), Olives, Nuts (and nut oils), Natural Peanut Butter
Polyunsaturated	Fatty Fish (Tuna, Herring, Salmon, Mackerel, Trout, Sardines and Fish or Krill Oils), Walnuts (and Oil), Flaxseed (and Oil), Sunflower Seeds, Sesame Seeds, Pumpkin Seeds, Soymilk and Tofu
Saturated	Red Meat (Beef, Lamb, Pork), Coconut Oil, Yogurt, Cheese, Animal Milks, Butter, Ghee

Similar to proteins it's recommended to source raw, wild, organic, and grass-fed fats whenever possible, to maximize the health benefits.

The Bad – Trans Fats
Trans fats cause inflammation, which is responsible for a host of chronic diseases including coronary disease, stroke, and diabetes. They mess with your cholesterol, both kinds, spiking them in the wrong direction, lowering your HDL, while raising the LDL. It's not without some irony that a lot of the biggest culprits of trans fats in our diets today came to prominence as a replacement for the good natural fats listed above, which were demonized at the time.

Trans fats are sneaky and put in pretty much everything you buy off-the-shelf in a standard convenience store or supermarket.

It's even the reason why a certain famous fast-food chains' fries don't taste so good anymore, they switched from cooking in delicious (and natural) beef tallow to vegetable oil.

Bad Fat Sources

Trans Fats	Vegetable Oils, Margarine, Commercial Fried Foods (fries, chicken, fish), Commercial pastries (donuts, cookies, biscuits), Commercial Snacks (chips, crackers, microwave popcorn, vegetable straws), Hydrogenated or Partially Hydrogenated Oils, Vegetable Shortening

Vegetables

Vegetables have been a disrespected, neglected afterthought for much of western dietary history. In households where I grew up vegetables were an overcooked side dish, often consisting of bland potatoes, carrots, broccoli, or peas; almost always boiled to death making them easy to eat for those of us without teeth. Lucky for us and our health that mentality has largely faded in the new millennium. Nowadays, most restaurants I visit have a newfound respect and focus on vegetables which in turn trickles down to our at-home eating habits. Take note of your own body and mind reactions when you have different vegetables – not all may be suited for all individuals (e.g., vegetables with a high-sulphur content i.e., broccoli, cauliflower, and beets may be great for some, but not others.)

Reasons to adore vegetables:

1. **Variety** – No other food has such a variety of types, tastes, and textures. When walking through markets or the aisles

of grocery stores, I continuously notice more and more vegetables of all shapes and sizes. One of my favorite things to do is grab a bunch of new ones, often having no idea what they are, and trying to figure out how to prepare them.

2. **Versatility** – Following on the point above, vegetables are incredibly versatile. Most can be prepared in limitless ways (raw, roasted, grilled, pickled, etc.), each preparation completely changing the texture and flavor profiles. Fresh vegetables, unlike a lot of fruits, can be stored for a decent amount of time, particularly roots and tubers.

3. **Cost** – Vegetables are crazy cheap compared to the other food categories on this list, particularly if you stick to the local and in-season rule, which is a win-win. Yes, you can pay a pretty penny for something imported and flown a few thousand miles which won't taste half as good as it would fresh, but overall, veggies are a cheap way to pack your body full of nutrients and good stuff.

4. **Nutrition** – This is a no-brainer. Ever since you were a little kid, your parents, teachers, doctors, and even your government have been telling you to eat more vegetables. As an individual who tends to question things, particularly those which come from authority figures and institutions, I buy into this advice wholeheartedly. The evidence is overwhelming, vegetables are full of nutrient-dense, vitamin-rich, folate (folic acid), potassium, fiber, antioxidants, disease-fighting phytonutrients, and chemicals. Like the varieties of vegetables themselves, the nutritional benefits are almost limitless.

Fruits

Fruits can be a little more complex than vegetables and depending on where in the world you live, the ease and cost of getting them fresh and in-season can be challenging. Similar to vegetables, there is a huge variety of fruits available all with different flavor profiles and health benefits. Generally, fruits have far greater amounts of carbohydrates and sugars than vegetables (avocados and olives being two notable exceptions) – but in wild and natural forms, which your body is accustomed to and nowhere near in the same class as refined grains, carbohydrates, and sugars. It's still recommended to consume your fruits whole, and not as a juice (e.g., orange juice) mainly because juices alone give you a big blast of those natural sugars (assuming there are no sugars added) while cutting out a lot of the vitamins and fibers found in the pulp, pith, or peel. The same goes for those tasty dried fruit snacks – while delicious, they're not much more than a slightly healthier candy, so limit your intake.

GRAINS & CUTTING CORNERS

Wheat, Corn, and Rice – Three cornerstones of the western diet and across much of the globe. All three are broadly classified as grains. A whole grain consists of three base elements:

- **The Bran** – The tough, shell-like outer layer, which contains fiber, minerals, and antioxidants.

- **The Germ** – The core of the grain, loaded with nutrients, the part new plants sprout from. Stocked with proteins, healthy fats, minerals, antioxidants, and other essential nutrients.

- **The Endosperm** – The bulk of the grain, containing mostly starchy carbs and a small amount of protein.

Most of us consume these three elements in refined versions which remove the bran and germ, leaving only the bulky and nutrient-lacking endosperm. In a nutshell, the fuel that makes up the bulk of the standard western diet removes all of the good stuff and leaves you with high-carb, high-calorie starch or what's commonly referred to as 'empty calories.' To make matters worse, due to the separation of the fiber (bran) and processing, the fuel is broken down by your body much faster than when in its natural form leading to spikes in blood sugar. True to the adage, what goes up must come down, your blood sugar plummets, leaving you hungry and craving more food. Thus, eating this type of food consistently leads to overeating, weight gain, and obesity.

"From a nutrition standpoint, there is **nothing** positive about refined grains."

– KRIS GUNNAR BSC MEDICINE AND NUTRITION RESEARCHER.

Which Grains Should I Eat, and Which Should I Avoid?

Natural, 'Wild' Grains – The Good	Oatmeal & Oats, Barley, Brown Rice, Wild Rice, Popcorn, Quinoa, Millet, Buckwheat, Bulgar, Whole Rye, Freekah, Amaranth, Kamut
Refined, Processed Grains – The Bad	White Flour (e.g. Bread, Muffins, Cakes, Cookies, Breakfast Cereals, Bagels, English Muffins, Crumpets, Biscuits), White Rice, Pasta

I LIKE MY SUGAR SWEET

Ok, plain and simple – lay off the sugars as much as possible. Especially added and refined sugars, think of it for what it is: **Candy**. You cannot subsist on candy, you shouldn't be making an entire meal of candy, you definitely shouldn't be living off of candy, and you probably shouldn't be eating it every day. Candy or sweets or lollies or whatever name you wish to call them is intended to be a treat, something to have on special occasions, not a dietary staple. It's a difficult thing to avoid and cut-out completely, and I have mad respect for those who manage to do so – I like sweet things, I have trouble avoiding a slice of apple pie from a good diner or an ice cream on a hot summer day, but those are treats, not daily occurrences. If you make your best effort to avoid as much sugar as possible, particularly the refined ones, your body and mind will be better off for it and they'll show their appreciation by performing better for you.

Sugars are empty calories – when added to food, they increase the caloric content without adding any nutritional value. Foods with a larger calorie count but less nutrition result in a greater chance of weight gain. Sugars are digested very quickly, meaning contrary to popular opinion they are not a good source of energy and instead will produce a quick sugar rush followed by a sugar crash.

Too much sugar can cause a multitude of ailments ranging from weight gain, diabetes, and may increase your risk of heart disease. The sugar industry is powerful and insidious, as a result, sugar hides everywhere, well-disguised under many names such as Sucrose, Fructose, Agave Nectar, Dextrose, Evaporated Cane Juice, Corn Syrup, Honey, Molasses, Treacle,

Corn Sweetener, Maltose, Lactose, Glucose, Maltodextrin, Fruit Juice Concentrate... and that's just a few to watch out for.

THE LIQUIDS

Water

Water. The end. Kidding. But this really should be the bulk of your liquid intake – cheap and readily available for most of us in the developed world. Be it from a tap, a filter, a box or a bottle, water is the be-all and end-all when it comes to hydration. You can have it still or sparkling, infused, or au naturel, but find what works for you to get more of it into your body and make it the core liquid you consume.

Coffee & Tea

What a godsend coffee is. The reliable sidekick to many great works of art, leaps in science,and engineering over the last few centuries. Long maligned, coffee has now rightly claimed its place as a superfood – Energy, mental acuity, essential nutrients, polyphenols, and antioxidants all packed into a cup. It tastes great hot or cold, can be used for cooking (I add it to chili) and the grinds make a great beef rub (good quality coffee grinds, smoked paprika, salt, and pepper).

Yes, it's got caffeine – which can be both good and bad. Good for alertness and mental acuity, bad for sleep and recovery. Caffeine has a sustained half-life almost magically adapted to our 24-hour day cycle with regular consumers' minds and bodies being prepped and ready for their dose every morning. For that reason alone you should try to limit your intake after noon. I'm one of those people who doesn't feel any noticeable effects from caffeine but rarely do I consume any after 2-3pm. Caffeine is far and away the most regularly consumed drug in the world, mostly via coffee, tea and (ugh) soda. Michael Pollan's short and easily digestible audiobook, 'Caffeine,' is a quick listen should you want to delve further into the subject.

Tea is another good form of hydration. When referring to tea, we're generally speaking of the orange pekoes, English breakfasts, oolongs, Darjeeling, and green tea varieties of the world. Green and black tea varieties all contain varying amounts of caffeine (albeit not as much as coffee), L-Theanine, and other nutrients and polyphenols. Herbal and Roobios teas don't contain caffeine, or if they do, only trace amounts.

An important element in keeping coffee and tea consumption as healthy as possible is to avoid adding the usual suspects to them – No milk, cream, or sugar. Just black, or to quote Agent Cooper from Twin Peaks, "As God intended." If you must have some form of sweetener or something creamy to offset coffee's acidity, try a small amount of honey, maple syrup, or oat milk. A St*rb*cks Caramel Macchiato is not a coffee, it bears more resemblance to a milkshake or a dessert.

That said, you can get really creative with coffee additives – I'm notorious for trying different experiments in my morning coffee often involving loud blender noises early in the morning. Some natural additives you can try experimenting with:

- MCT (Medium-Chain Triglycerides) Oil – Usually derived from coconut oil, a key component in 'bulletproof' coffee. Flavorless, but after blending the emulsified fats will give your coffee a frothy and creamy taste and appearance.

- Collagen Protein – The most common protein in the body, provides structure to bones, skin, tendons, and ligaments. Flavorless and an easy way to get an early morning dose of this important protein before training.

- Cinnamon – Unique taste, lowers blood sugar, antioxidants, and anti-inflammatory

- Cacao (not Cocoa!) – Chocolatey flavor, magnesium, nitric oxide to reduce fatigue and give you more energy, polyphenols, and antioxidants

- L-Theanine – Naturally occurring in both green and black teas enhance focus when paired with caffeine, reduces stress and anxiety (counteracting any potential 'jitters') and a host of other health benefits

- Mushroom Powder – Mushrooms rule the world. There are countless types and varieties of fungus and mycelia, many of which we still have little to no idea as to their effects when consumed. But the unique health benefits of certain mushrooms such as Lion's Mane, Cordyceps, Chaga, Reishi, and others have been known to communities around the globe for years. A benefit of global interconnectivity is in the sharing of this knowledge and as a result there are many readily available mushroom blends (usually as powders) which you can add to any food or drink you choose.

- Egg – I know it sounds strange, but throw some hot coffee in a blender, drop in an egg, whip it up and watch the huge froth that results. Basically a coffee egg creme combining the amazing benefits of nature's multivitamin with its amazing combination of proteins, fats, and nutrients with those of the coffee. A real protein shake and meal-in-a-cup!

Alcohol

I admit it's a tough one. Again, my respect goes out to those who forgo the stuff altogether, we definitely don't need it and it absolutely does not help our mind or body to perform at optimal levels. But again, moderation and making smart choices in the alcohols you do consume will go a long way. Some amount of effort and discipline is much better than simply giving up and doing nothing.

Principles to drink by:

1. **Don't drink every day**. If this is difficult for you start by making a schedule of the days when you can or cannot drink and stick to it. Remember, the only person you'll be cheating is yourself.

2. **Don't binge drink** until you're drunk, hammered, blotto or whatever term you want to use. We've all done it and we all regret it afterward, simply stop.

3. **Drink a full glass of water between every alcoholic drink**. It'll slow your consumption and keep you hydrated, helping flush out the alcohol toxins and sugars.

4. **Drink lower-sugar and lower-calorie drinks** – and by this I don't mean light beer or artificial chemical loaded 'light' pre-mixed cocktails. Don't drink cocktails. Don't drink beer. Instead trying sticking to wine or unmixed liquors. If you need a mixer or something to dilute the alcohol, use ice, water, or soda water – not fruit juice or soda. Alcohol is the

result of fermenting sugars, you don't need to top sugar with more sugar.

Soda & Fruit Juices
Avoid them. There's a lot of alternative options out there, from infused waters, still or sparkling, teas, coffees (even decaf!), kombucha and kefir-based fermented drinks. They will better refresh your thirst and your body and mind will thank you.

FASTING

The prominence of fasting has seen a significant rise in popular culture recently, while a good trend, in reality fasting is nothing new. Consider how long the human species has existed, estimates range from tens of thousands to a couple of hundred thousand years, what fraction of those have we been able to walk to the fridge, cupboard, pantry, or corner cafe to grab a bite first thing in the morning? This is a twentieth-century convenience or at best a century or so. Once food production and sales became a business we were off the races, with marketing phrases such as "Breakfast is the most important meal of the day!" running rampant. And what a campaign it was, surely one of the most successful marketing strategies ever as decades on people repeat those words like a spiritual mantra and take it for a fact. Dr. John Harvey Kellogg (the same one of Kellogg's cereal fame) is credited with inventing the slogan and he was quite a character with some suspect beliefs regarding sexuality and other aspects of human nature. His classic Corn Flakes product (refined and processed grains) was created in his search for something to dull and blunt the libido.

Back to the point, for 99% of human existence we did not wake up and eat. We'd wake up, drink some water from a nearby river or stream before beginning a long day of hunting and gathering in hopes of collecting enough food to survive another day. I find it interesting that when you look at paintings or even photographs available before the twentieth century, how rare it is to see an obese person, and those you do happen across tend to be very wealthy individuals or royalty, who could afford such gluttonous excess. Today it's a different story when you walk around any major western city, the obesity epidemic is out of control. Our bodies are adapted and designed for operating on extended periods without food.

In a fasted state, your body does some amazing things:

- Insulin levels drop in your blood promoting blood sugar control and fat burning

- Human growth hormone (HGH) levels increase exponentially, up to 5x – helping with both fat burning and muscle gain (fasting helps increase muscle!)

- Reduces inflammation levels to promote overall health

- Helps remove waste from cells, facilitating repairs of stronger, healthier cells

- Increases gene expressions relating to longevity and disease resistance (delaying aging and living longer)

- Potential to improve brain function and reduce the likelihood of neurodegenerative disorders. May increase the growth of new neurons and help protect the brain from damage

The most common form of fasting practiced today is intermittent fasting, a relatively painless form of fasting and easy to adapt to while still getting a lot of the above-mentioned benefits. The simplest form is known as 16:8 – You have an 8-hour window where you eat and a 16-hour window where you don't. E.g., You eat your first meal at noon and finish your last meal (and snacks) by 8pm. This isn't very difficult, particularly if you're sleeping for 8 of those hours. You really only have to deal with a few hours on either side of waking during which you can consume all the water, coffee, or tea (without milk or cream) you like.

SUMMARY

The importance of how you fuel your mind and body cannot be understated. It never ceases to amaze me the amount of time and effort we will put into trivial purchases that have minimal effects on our lives but what we eat and drink is almost an afterthought. The amount of 'convenience food' littering the aisles of our grocery stores and hawked on restaurant menus is staggering and worrying. I have no doubt an ample portion of the billions spent on healthcare could be significantly reduced if we paid a little more attention in taking care of what we put into our bodies as fuel.

It's up to you to adjust your diet and apply aspects of the above advice in manageable ways to help you. Try them out, shift them around and pay attention to when you're more alert and energetic, feeling better about yourself, and how you're operating.

None of us are superhuman and it can be difficult to integrate numerous large changes and habitual shifts in a short period, instead pick a few – perhaps the ones you feel will make the biggest difference along with those that you already do or will find easy. A final reminder that the most significant message in The Savage Discipline is being adaptable to the world around you and circumstances that come up. Don't chastise yourself for missing a target or a goal, if you can manage to stick to your chosen guidelines and nourish your mind and body 80% of the time you've already made a big step forward in your health and performance.

One of the base tenants of The Savage Discipline is that the mind and body cannot be viewed as separate entities, they are forever interconnected and entwined. This is evidenced by the fact that if either one is sick or diminished in function it will affect the other. The human body is built for movement and our success as hunters and gatherers across the plains of Africa and beyond, speaks to this. Our ancestors relied on cunning as well as endurance and stamina combined with a lithe and strong musculature system to run down, capture or trap their prey. Exercise was a necessity for survival throughout most of our history. The modern sedentary lifestyle didn't really appear until the last century or so for anyone except the wealthiest and most privileged of individuals.

Then came industrialization and with it lines of travel and communication expanded – the locomotive, the automobile, the telephone, and so on through the present day where many of us rarely walk anywhere, instead sitting at desks and staring at screens for the bulk of our day. The results of such a societal shift are now so obvious, there's no need to look at any studies – people are obese, sick, anxious, and depressed at levels unseen at any time or place throughout history. All in the midst of constant revolutions and leaps forward in medicine, engineering, and science.

Our natural reaction to this epidemic has been to take up forms of exercise and training traditionally relegated to the realm of athletes – jogging, cycling, gym classes, personal trainers, and strength training. This is a great trend and something sorely needed to combat our sedentary times, but it's not easy for everyone, on the contrary, It's not really easy for anyone, it requires work, commitment, and discipline. The Williams sisters, LeBron James, Michael Phelps, and Connor McDavid's of the world surely have days where they're too tired or don't want to do it. We all know The Pain of Beginning vs. The Pleasure of Finishing and it's keeping those end results in perspective that helps hone your focus and commitment.

The Savage Discipline promotes exercise and activity of both the mind and the body, each and every day. This doesn't mean you need to go all out every day – sleep, rest and recovery are one of the legs on that three-legged stool, alongside exercise and nutrition. But you need to move and activate your body in some way every single day. Be it a walk around the block, doing a few squats, push-ups and sit-ups after waking, or whatever feels right for you. On active rest days I tend to do some form of hike or climbing, or if I'm stuck at home or in a hotel without a gym, I'll do a core or bodyweight circuit.

There's a limitless amount of group activities where you can exercise both body and mind, from team sports, fitness classes, to yoga, etc. This book focuses on exercises you can do on your own, without any formal group, class or buddy required – pinning all the responsibility (and success) on yourself. It's not going to be easy and it requires dedication and hard work. You're sure to experience days when you 'just don't feel like it,' you're feeling under the weather, or your body is already sore from exercising. Well tough, that's life, and being adaptable and working through the challenges that arise is a major part of it. You need to push through it for yourself. I promise you'll feel better physically and mentally after you get it done. The sense of accomplishment combined with the endorphins rushing through your body will make you question why you were ever reluctant to get moving in the first place (but don't worry, you'll be reluctant again tomorrow or the day after).

As I fast approach my mid-forties, I cherish the opportunities to pit myself against those in the so-called prime of life, and more often than not I come out on top. That success comes down to a combination of will, belief, and the thorough training regimen I diligently follow. It combines the four F's: Functional, Flexible, Fight, and Flight.

FUNCTIONAL

A term that's often bandied about of late; to clarify any misunderstandings my definition of 'Functional' is as follows: A variety of natural movements, lifts, pulls, and pushes to place resistance on your body, resulting in increased strength, range of motion, balance, and stability over time.

Running, cycling and similar activities offer a host of benefits, training numerous muscle groups while strengthening cardiovascular health and endurance. Yoga has countless variants and styles to suit any individual taste while building strength, balance, presence of mind, and flexibility. However, a missing component from most of the aforementioned exercise methods is weight-loaded resistance training – which is important to include in your training at every phase or stage of life. Every day we're required to lift and move things around, particularly our own bodies. Many of us don't give a second thought to motions such as standing up or sitting down, carrying something home from the store, or climbing a flight of stairs. Each of these everyday movements incorporates a different set of strong and flexible muscles, joints and ligaments, weight-bearing skeletal structure, solid balance, and core strength. With this is mind, there is no better physical preparation against aging than strength and resistance training.

Compound exercises are a great place to start, working multiple muscles and joints, ultimately emulating movements you do throughout daily life. The added weight ensures you can continue to do those movements with relative ease and little effort. Form is important when performing compound exercises, not only for safety, but something even professional athletes are continuously fine-tuning to ensure maximum efficiency. This also keeps the exercises fresh and adds an aspect of mental focus. Just like running, cycling or any of your favorite cardio exercises they too get your heart rate firing and burn calories in addition to strengthening muscles and increasing coordination – more 'bang for your buck', particularly when you get more advanced and work in super or giant sets.

Common Compound Exercises include: Squats, Bench Press, Deadlift, Pull-Ups, Rows, Dips, and Overhead Presses.

Figure 1: Barbell Back Squat

Figure 2: Barbell Bench Press

Stay Fresh: Every 8-16 weeks, as you start to get (too) comfortable with your routines you need to change things up – keep your mind and body guessing, adapting, growing, and progressing. Online you can find a wealth of free content and routines made available by professional trainers and physiotherapists ensuring inspiration and ideas for routines are not lacking; the important thing is to keep it fun and challenging, helping you stay committed and reaping the benefits of the training. To get you started I've provided a few simple tweaks you can add to your routines to keep them fresh while pushing your mind and body into new ranges of motion utilizing different muscle groups:

Off-Balance: One of my favorite twists, these movements are quite advanced and can be tricky when you first attempt them. Ensure you stay safe and initially try them with very a low weight before working your way up. There's several methods of throwing yourself off balance:

- Off-Set: Load up a single side of a barbell – this is guaranteed to garner you a lot of strange looks at the gym and from time to time you'll even have a well-meaning individual warn you that you've forgotten to load up the other side. Ignore the looks and press on (no pun intended), this is the stuff the Savage Discipline is made of. If you can load a barbell on one side only while executing a perfect squat, lunge (forward & reverse), overhead press, row, and bench press you are doing some serious functional movements with your body *and* focus with your mind. It doesn't matter how much weight your lifting, this is *much* more difficult to execute than a perfectly balanced, symmetrical lift.

Figure 3: Off-Set Barbell Back Squat

- Bosu Ball: Again, this is so much fun. Writing about these moves makes me want to start doing them – which is great, as it represents how training can become something both rewarding and enjoyable to do and not simply a chore. Just like the above, perform the exercise and maintain perfect form while standing on the flat side of a Bosu Ball (the rounded portion should be on the ground). You'll be destabilizing yourself and forced to recruit more underutilized muscles to compensate. Too easy? You can increase the difficulty by performing naturally off-balanced, one-armed or one-legged exercises, e.g. Try a one-armed clean and jerk's with a barbell on the Bosu Ball, this results in a highly-advanced exercise that will require all of your focus and recruit so many different muscles it's almost a full-body workout in a single exercise.

- If you really want to take the off-balance stuff to the next level (and have a high enough ceiling), you can try the above mentioned Bosu Ball method but swap the Bosy for a completely spherical Swiss or Medicine ball or two. To ramp this up even further you could try combining the Swiss or Bosu Ball techniques with the initial off-balance one, but again, be safe!

Off-balance work maximizes the 'functional' aspect of functional training – how often in life do you need to lift, pick-up, push, or pull something that is perfectly symmetrical and evenly balanced? Off-balance work replicates real-world situations requiring real-world strength, flexibility and focus. It will work your core and stabilization muscles much harder as they'll be firing in all sorts of unusual ways to compensate for the asymmetric weight distribution in trying to balance the load.

The aforementioned techniques are just the tip of the iceberg. Experiment with different movements and styles, steal moves from other people – there's so much free information available just waiting for you to use. Find what you like, what inspires and challenges you. I'll reiterate that you need to make it fun and once you do you'll see how quickly it becomes a habit.

FLEXIBLE

Two forms of flexibility are important here – Your body, muscles, and limbs, and the often overlooked methods, places, and equipment you use to train.

Physical Flexibility

Just as essential as strength training, particularly as your body ages and you want to maintain the full range of motion in your joints, ligaments, and muscles. If you're beginning your physical fitness journey in your thirties or later, meaning you've commenced the heroic task of changing your habits and lifestyle from non-active (aka couch potato) to fit and healthy, you'll want to ensure you focus on stretching and limbering up your body, limbs, and muscles both before and after your training. Gentle forms of yoga that are excellent for this, focusing on breath work (underrated and essential) and flows designed to get your body moving to its maximum ability. It can be a discouraging setback when you attempt to get fit and healthy but push too quickly, get injured and end up severely restricted to low-impact exercises for a few months while you recover, so I implore you not to ignore this aspect.

If you've been training for years or decades chances are you've got your systems down and your body is accustomed to moving in a variety of ways, but it doesn't hurt anyone to try some new forms of stretching and limbering up before and after training; particularly before attempting something new. Every professional athlete does this, so it should be a no-brainer. Foam rollers and tennis balls can be great tools when trying to stretch specific muscles and loosen up tight spots. If you can afford the luxury of a certified sports masseuse, it's well worth the treat.

Training Flexibility
"The person who really wants to do something finds a way; the other person finds an excuse."

I stand by that quote but also believe you should give yourself an advantage – remove any options for excuses and have a backup plan ready for any circumstances that may arise. I write this section from my London home during lockdown due to the COVID-19 sweeping the globe. My gym is closed and has been for almost two months. The outdoor calisthenic areas at the park nearby has been fenced off for a similar amount of time. This sounds like the perfect excuse to take a break, stop training and blame it on the situation, right? Nope. Instead I changed up my routine and because I didn't want to lose the muscle, flexibility, and endurance I'd worked so hard to gain, I increased my training schedule to a full seven days a week while rotating muscle groups and push/pull activity to ensure adequate rest.

As anyone who's been to London is aware, there's not a lot of space – it's a crowded urban metropolis with too many people squeezed into a small area with roads and transportation systems that were not designed to cope with such loads. This results in many small houses and apartments with limited space, so you really have to get creative when the world suddenly decides to close down and you have to add a fully functioning gym to your living area. I have a barbell and two dumbbells with about 60kg/132lbs of plates, a few kettlebells (up to 16kg/35lbs), and a resistance band – all of that cost less than £150/$180 and can be stored under a couch or bed. That equipment, along with one of the benches from my dining room table is enough to create dozens of different routines targeting every muscle group. If you don't believe me do a quick Internet search for "kettlebell routines" or "resistance band training" and see what I mean.

The restrictions placed upon me with limited equipment and weight forced me to change and adapt, creating entirely new routines based on what was available. It completely shifted my training regimen forcing my mind and body to learn new techniques and hit different muscles in different ways than ever before. It ended up being a *good thing*, getting me out of my comfort zone and expanding my repertoire. A perfect example of which I'll delve into further in the Limitations & Restrictions chapter.

The easy path is to make an excuse, but again, the only person you're cheating is yourself. A resistance band weighs nothing and can fit in any bag that you can take with you anywhere. A good fifteen minutes of training is at least fifteen times better than doing nothing at all.

FIGHT

Training is not meant to be easy; you need to feel it. The reason you're training, be it your mind or your muscles, is to grow, expand, and increase your capabilities and knowledge. You may have heard the expression 'growing pains,' well, this is what they're talking about.

Regardless of how naturally inclined or talented you are in certain areas once you reach a certain level or plateau progression is hard. It requires diligence, focus and effort just to get a 1% increase but those are the kind of margins that separate the average from the exceptional. Something that one individual can do with relative ease may be difficult for others and vice versa. Rather than discouraging you you need to train your mind to rise to the challenge as overcoming them will feel that much sweeter.

The fight is a mental aspect and not solely focused on continuously working out. Forcing yourself to rest, take days off, rotating motions and muscle groups is equally important. You will inevitably find certain aspects of training easier and more enjoyable than others and you'll naturally gravitate towards them. You have to fight those instincts to ensure you're training different parts of your body in different ways while allowing them sufficient time to rest and recover. You need to keep shaking things up and not fall into a training rut – if you look back and realize you've been doing the same routines day in and day out for 4-6 months or longer you really need to change things up. There's limitless resources available for free online, as well as personal trainers, magazines, etc. If you train at a gym you can take note of interesting maneuvers other gym-goers are doing, copy or modify them to integrate into your own routine.

Short on time? Want to create a workout to minimize time, maximize muscle growth, and get cardio in as well? Super and Giant sets are my favored method of achieving this and other than days when I'm solely training for strength (i.e., lifting heavier weight) which requires more rest, I almost exclusively do both to get maximum bang for my buck.

Supersets are when you perform two exercises back to back, for example, you'll do 8 reps of a bench press and without rest follow it with 8 reps of a goblet squat, equaling one set in total after which you can rest for an allotted period. Giant sets are similar but they add more exercises back to back essentially amounting to a mini-circuit, a core or abdominal-focused giant set I perform is as follows – 10 x weighted (I use a medicine ball) leg raises on a bench (to achieve negative decline), followed by 15 x weighted knee crunches (using the same medicine ball on the same bench), followed by 12 x weighted leg pull-ins (using a dumbbell), and then quickly shifting to 12 x bodyweight leg pull-ins – these last two amount to what's known as a 'drop set.' If you perform three sets of the above you're getting just short of 150 reps targeting different groups of abdominal muscles in about 10 minutes of work.

FLIGHT

The final piece of the physical training puzzle. How do you really take your physical training to the next level enabling optimal performance and, in a sense, allow yourself to take flight? You need to start tackling all those little bits and pieces that 99% of gym-goers ignore; think of them as the intangibles, because they separate the wheat from the chaff, but they are in fact very tangible indeed. The factors we're discussing here are things like speed, explosiveness, endurance, and reaction training, or SEER.

Speed, Explosiveness, Endurance, and Reaction (SEER) Training

The idea we've been working towards here is to mould and hone yourself into a lean mean fighting machine; best prepared to adapt to any circumstance or curveballs life may throw at you – be that an ad-hoc meeting, getting lost in a remote jungle, or fighting your way through a zombie apocalypse. No matter which of those you encounter, speed will help you conquer it – thinking, moving, and reacting quickly to any situation.

You may have come across the term 'Interval Training' or 'HIIT,' an acronym for High Impact Interval Training. This form of training has become popular as it's a great way to perform an intense workout in a short period of time while also working those elusive elements of speed and explosiveness. In a nutshell, HIIT training is a short high-speed intense period of exercise alternating with a longer period of less intensive 'recovery'-type exercise repeated for several sets. For example, you sprint as fast as possible for 30 seconds and then slow to a walking pace for 90 seconds, running through the entire cycle 10 times. The example I just gave is probably the most common type of HIIT training there is, and perhaps the most boring too. So make it interesting, try alternating 10 fast 40cm box jumps with 5 slow one-legged 60cm box jumps per leg. Or maybe 10 high-speed burpees followed 5 ultra-slow one-legged squats per leg. Spinning classes tend to be a natural HIIT activity, and for something with a little more adrenaline try outdoor trail running or mountain biking. All of the above will work your speed, explosiveness, and reaction skills to the max.

Speed & Agility Ladders are cheap, portable tools tailor-made for working the types of training mentioned above. You can use them for footwork as you may have seen professional athletes do, or again get more creative with them, doing different types of push-ups or squats in, out, and around the ladder.

The definition of Endurance is "the ability to endure an unpleasant or difficult process or situation without giving way." If you pause and think about that for a moment the potential ways to increase endurance and stamina become apparent. You need to train your mind and body to sustain periods of resistance or discomfort, to get comfortable or acclimatized to being in those positions so they don't seem as unpleasant anymore. Jogging or running may be the most classic method of endurance training and for good reason, it works. You can do it almost anywhere and increase the difficulty by adding hills (both inclines and declines to work balance and recruit different muscles), or even obstacles. Swimming and cycling get you similar benefits and you can also make them as challenging or leisurely as you please.

Some less common methods of endurance training and strength-endurance training in particular, include high-intensity circuits (Design your own! Join a class! Try one of those So-and-

So Bootcamps!); but you can even make slight modifications to your current training to focus on endurance rather than strength – the keys to improving your endurance are frequency and duration. To get those two aspects ramped up try lowering the amount of weight you're using (enabling you to do more reps) and reducing the amount of rest between sets (allowing for more sets). For example, on a hypertrophy training day you may bench press 60kg/132lbs for 3 sets each with 8 reps. If you wanted to work on increasing the endurance of the muscles on a different day of the week (not the day directly before or after), try lowering the weight to 40kg/88lbs for 5 sets each with 12-15 reps, ramping up both the frequency and duration of strain on those same muscles.

SUMMARY

Moving your body affects your brain, plain and simple. There's a lot of studies and data out there pointing to ideas generated while walking or focusing on some physical task, leaving your mind less occupied and open to generating unique or previously unthought-of connections. In my experience, contrary to what you'd expect, when you're feeling lethargic, low, or even sick (or hungover), getting out and sweating it out is a true cure-all. Get yourself off the couch, out of that rut, and really take note of how you feel afterward, showered, refreshed, blood and oxygen pumping, muscles warmed and limber – it's so simple but it truly is amazing how much it can feel like a rebirth.

"Robert Johnson, even more so. Robert was one of the most inventive geniuses of all time. But he probably had no audience to speak of. He was so far ahead of his time that we still haven't caught up with him. His status today couldn't be any higher. Yet in his day, his songs must have confused people. It just goes to show you that *great people follow their own path*"

– BOB DYLAN NY TIMES
JUNE 12TH, 2020

This is your work, not simply the job you go to everyday (though perhaps it should be?), but your life's work and the legacy you wish to leave behind. Everyone needs a purpose, it's the primary factor of a fulfilling life. Without purpose we feel listless, lost, and adrift.

What do you want your days to be about? Working your nose to the grindstone at a job you don't like for forty years to make a lot of money which you're too burnt out to spend when you finally do retire? It won't matter as you will have spent so much time and effort on the kind of work you've just left behind that you won't even know what to do with yourself.

Perhaps you justify it by living for the weekend, always relishing TGIF, or waiting for a vacation – but is living your life in a perpetual cycle of waiting for less than 30% of the scraps really what you want? Wouldn't you rather get at least a passing grade or as close to 100% as possible? Life is about the journey, each and every day counts, learning, experiencing, enjoying, contributing; doing things that matter to you, your community, and beyond. Make it count.

As the title of the book states, Discipline is a big part of it. I'm aware of the trends toward being kind and gentle to yourself, taking it easy and taking your time. While I wholeheartedly agree with much of that message, in that we need rest, downtime, and should always be kind to ourselves and others; every yin has its yang. There's a time to buckle down and focus, force some new habits, and get to work – I find no higher calling and I wholeheartedly believe it's what we're here to do – **to produce our very best work**. Besides, if we're talking about being kind to ourselves isn't working to ensure we're happy, contributing and finding purpose the ultimate form of such kindness?

We're living in a world of distraction where there's limitless time-vampire intrusions vying for your attention. Focus is hard at the best of times even when alone in a cabin by a lake without any electricity, but in the midst of the daily hustle and bustle of everyday life? The odds are stacked against you. Be kind to yourself by striving to take something back, get back to the simple ways, put on blinders and ignore things (e.g., I don't watch or read the news, I don't use Facebook). **Say "No" a lot**.

Priority was originally a singular word until sometime in the twentieth century we bastardized it, turning it into "priorities," which makes little sense if you pause to think about it – how can you even have more than one priority? Use the tiny amount of time you have on this planet with care – it's so fleeting and precious you absolutely need to be protective of it. The only person you're cheating is yourself, a better, more productive and happier you will have a fast trickle-down effect to those around you.

When researching purpose three contributing factors came up again and again. Sometimes the wording was slightly different but the core meaning and values clearly resonated with many individuals enabling one to define a formula for finding and determining a sense of purpose. It may surprise you to learn that neither money, status, nor fame have much, if anything, to do with finding a truly satisfying purpose. In fact, it's not so much about taking as it is giving back. Here we have yet again another three-legged stool where each leg is just as important as the next; remove any one and the entire structure tumbles to the ground.

CURIOSITY

Many of the most creative historical figures didn't dogmatically focus their efforts on a single work or operated within a single field. Instead they flit from one on endeavor to the next and back again always following their curiosity. Some may take this for a lack of focus or dedication but I disagree – How many would accuse the likes of Leonardo Da Vinci, Nikola Tesla, or even Elon Musk of such a character flaw? Instead, it's the innate childlike curiosity and the vision to pursue it (often against all odds) that leads to breakthroughs and many works now regarded as genius.

SKILL

Of course, not just anyone can paint a Mona Lisa or architect an awe-inspiring structure. You need at least the basics, some core skills in the area (or areas) you wish to pursue. This needn't be daunting but rather part of the journey and fun. In most cases you don't need to become a virtuoso or reach the absolute pinnacle in the skills required but you do need to have a foundation and basic understanding to ensure you can execute what you need to do.

Fortunately, we are capable of learning the foundations of most skills quite rapidly, it's that final 10-20% peak that requires years of practice and dedication.

CONTRIBUTION

Perhaps the most overlooked piece is your contribution to society, be it on a local community or global scale. Knowing your efforts and work are helping in some way, becoming a part of a greater something – this is an elusive factor which makes one's work truly fulfilling. You can while away extra hours, days, or weeks working a project, immersing yourself in it because not only are you curious and skilled at it but you know it's going to make a difference to somebody, somewhere.

Marie Curie, the renowned scientist known for her contributions to the fight against cancer was often described as a "mad scientist" or a "maniacal worker" because of how insanely interested and immersed she was in her work, which she no doubt viewed as her purpose.

THE INTERSECTION

Though by no means an exact science, the intersection point of a classic Venn diagram can help guide your choices and direction towards finding purpose in your life. Simply jot down a list beside each of the above areas – What are you curious about? What skills do you have?

How can you contribute? And see where the overlaps are. It may not be glaringly obvious, you may have to dig a bit, and make some adjustments – E.g., if you find Curiosity & Contribution overlapping in several areas but you're lacking in some skills, perhaps it's time to start to researching, practicing, honing, and improving those latent areas. This is exactly the point of the exercise, to give you an idea and to show you how and where you can focus your energies to get where you want to go and increase your enjoyment of life. When you're happy and engaged in something, it's much easier to give your best effort and perform than when forced to do something against your will. When complete, your diagram should look something like this:

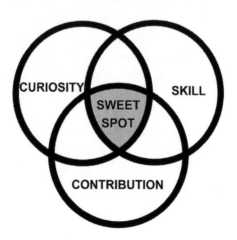

Throughout the course of your life and as you progress, grow, and learn, your purpose can shift or change. This is fine and absolutely normal, perhaps your purpose will naturally shift course and you'll go with the flow. If not, you can always reassess and return to the above exercise for ideas. Continue to follow and engage your curiosity, if something's not working don't just carry on. Instead, take a step back and determine why, then make any necessary adjustments to the program. You'd do the same for any other project you were working on, so why not for the most important and lifelong project of yourself? If you aren't honest with yourself you risk subpar performance and the individual you'll be letting down most is yourself.

BONUS POINTS

It can be difficult for all the pieces to fall perfectly into place, for the stars to align and to have your cake and eat it too. The three areas above are the core tenets, the foundations of that three-legged stool but beyond those, are there other factors you could consider? Of course there are, you could make an endless list of criteria and requirements so specific that you'd a) never find anything suitable, and b) will become discouraged even trying. Many of these aspects are what you'd call fringe elements, they add touches of comfort or luxury such as monetary or commercial value of your purpose. Such things aren't necessary, and I would recommend leaving them off your critical criteria list so as not to restrict your options; it's better to feel 80-90% fulfilled and purposeful, than zero.

With that in mind, there are two other pieces I'd elevate above fringe but below the three core elements and they are Collaboration and Flexibility.

Collaboration

We're a tribal species, it's how we've evolved both biologically and culturally. It will be a long while after you and I are gone before we evolve beyond those default settings. As such, if you can find elements of collaboration, communication, and maybe even friendship in your purpose, that's an excellent bonus.

Developing things in collaboration as well as having a sounding board and others to bounce ideas off of is a big advantage. It allows you those who share some of your curiosities, passions, and skills to give you feedback and chip in and assist as necessary. With that in mind you should still ensure you make time to figure out and discover things on your own – solutions, ideas and such. Different forms and types of ideas appear in different situations.

Flexibility

What better way to allow oneself to explore the world and follow your curiosity anywhere than a calling and purpose that allows for maximum flexibility? Aspects such as 'where' a purpose or function can be performed (remote vs. specific location, city vs. country, office vs. home, etc.) or can you work family or other commitments around it, etc. should be considered as bonuses (or detriments) as they can significantly effect your levels of engagement and happiness.

SUMMARY

There is no magic bullet for finding purpose; but one thing is certain, deep down inside we know when something isn't right. When you just aren't feeling it or it isn't working. We all have good days and bad days and it's worth remembering that we need to take things in stride and fully process them and not act rashly. But if you've got that nagging feeling, despising something for weeks, months, or even years on end, then it's time to shift things up and make a change, because no one else is going to do it for you. Sure, it may be risky but the alternative is not making any changes and growing ever more embittered and apathetic about your life and place in it, which really isn't any sort of option at all.

"We live in a world where there is more and more information and less and less meaning"

– JEAN BAUDRILLARD,
SIMULACRA AND SIMULATION.

After generating some ideas around purpose, you'll need to take back some of your day to ensure you can fulfil it. A particular phrase I detest is "I don't have time." A blatant cop-out and the worst excuse of any kind. Consider an average day and do an honest assessment of how much time of it is wasted on things such as social media, deciding what to watch (and watching) on your streaming service of choice, texting and chatting with friends, etc. It quickly becomes apparent that "I don't have time" is what we've deemed a socially acceptable and polite way of saying "No, that's not really important to me. It's not my priority."

Speaking of priorities, the evolution of the word itself exemplifies our societal trends. "Priority" is a singular word meaning something "of the utmost importance" or "the top of the heap," something that cannot be multiplied or pluralized because there is only one top! But how many times have you been asked to list your "priorities"? We've watered down the meaning of the word to a list of things which we acknowledge *may* be of some importance but chances are you rarely, if ever, get through that entire list.

Both are important concepts in planning and scheduling your day – you decide what is of utmost importance and absolutely must get done. That's your priority. If and when you complete that you can set a new priority, not before. If you deem a task too menial don't skirt around it saying "I don't have time." Instead, be honest, save some frustration and sub-standard work for yourself and whomever may be asking you by simply saying "No." Choosing to explain or justify your reasoning beyond that is up to you.

THE NIGHT BEFORE

A five-minute task – sometime in the evening get into the habit of having a look at your plan for the following day, be it some form of electronic calendar or a written schedule. This eases any anxiety and allows you to mentally prepare and order your plan of action for tomorrow. What you see (hopefully it isn't much a surprise), isn't something that should make you anxious or panic. Nobody's perfect and mistakes happen, for example, you see a presentation due tomorrow which you forgot about and didn't prepare. I get it – it sucks – but isn't it better to notice now, 10-12-14 hours earlier rather than 2-4 hours before? You now have time to mitigate the problem – send a quick email asking to push it back a few hours. Shift morning appointments and tasks to make room to work on it. Wake up earlier, call in supporting troops, etc. You have more time and more options. Chances are now that you've noticed and are in the habit of checking it's less likely to happen in the future.

PLANNING

Studies show, contrary to popular opinion, the majority of us cannot effectively multitask. The research reveals less than 2% of the population are able to multitask, but for this exercise we'll be generous and round up to 5% – either way, the odds are stacked against you. With that in mind, when planning your day don't overlap tasks or lump things together unless the item is so trivial and unimportant to you that you honestly don't mind if the quality slips. In which case, why is it on your list anyways? When switching between tasks it takes the mind and body time to recalibrate and become accustomed to the new processes, movements, and thoughts required and to get into a sense of flow. Think of it as a warm-up period prior to exercise or a musician or singer warming up their voice, fingers or embouchure before a performance. If you go out cold you're prone to subpar performance and even injury. None of us want to disappoint, we want to perform our best, delivering a stellar performance and winning at all costs.

When planning it's important to allot time for switching or readjusting to prepare for the next task. At a previous roles I noticed attendees were habitually late for meetings which had the trickle-down effect of meetings constantly overrunning to make up for lost time. This type of behavior drives me crazy, most of the time there's really no excuse and it simply comes down to a lack of respect for those waiting on you or bad time-keeping and organization on your part – neither being traits one would want to cultivate. Being only one person I was unable to halt the flow or redirect the entire river myself. Instead I made two adjustments to my own scheduling – I set meetings to commence at five minutes after the hour or half-hour (i.e., 10:05 or 10:35), and set them to end 15 minutes earlier than expected, usually a quarter to the hour. The bulk of people's calendars aren't zoomed in to notice such granular differences so they generally assume a 10:05 meeting commenced at 10:00. If they happened to arrive 5-10 minutes late this shrunk the amount of time wasted for both of us and should they be early or on-time, we could begin with time to spare. Similarly, the meeting close buffer of 15 minutes allowed one of two things to occur; the meeting could overrun without impacting any other appointments, while also providing a buffer to travel, dial-in, and prepare for your next meeting or task.

Make sure to plan breaks into your day. By this I meet adequate periods to disconnect, go for a walk, read a few pages, listen to a podcast and let your mind wander. Not a break meaning a working lunch or wolfing down a sandwich while staring at your emails. A real break is not wasted time, studies show time away from tasks, letting your mind drift and wander, focusing on other things fosters new neural connections and associations between seemingly unrelated tasks in your mind. There's a great example of this in the film, "The Theory of Everything," based on the life of renowned physicist and cosmologist, Stephen Hawking. Two scenes in particular – one in which he's simply watching the cream swirling into his black coffee leading him to theorize how black holes may be visible, and another in which he is struggling to pull a sweater over his head and viewing burning coals and embers in his fireplace through the sweater, coming up with the idea that 'if a black hole has entropy, then it ought to have a temperature.' While I can't confirm these scenes are reflective of the actual events (though the film was based on a book by Hawking's wife, Jane Wilde), the idea of regular, day-to-day life events connecting with and influencing higher aspects of your thinking and work is depicted brilliantly.

CHECKLISTS

Though we're sometimes reluctant to admit it, something in our nature loves lists – top 10's of whatever. They're conversation starters, good things to debate and argue the merits of such-and-such versus the other contenders. Beyond that kind of list many of us have to deal with a variety of To Do' lists, Shopping lists, or other checklists throughout our day. There's an innate feeling of accomplishment in checking things off a list, showing you're progressing and making headway towards your goals. The flip side being the feeling of disappointment and frustration when you fail to get those things done – for that reason some may find lists don't work for them or puts them in a worse state of mind with heightened feelings of anxiety.

I'm of the opinion that lists can work for most of us, though like many methods details herein you may have to tweak and make adjustments to find the method that best works for you. If it's making you anxious rather than increasing your level of comfort and accomplishment, make some changes. Simplify the list and make it high-level (e.g., Work, Exercise, Read).

Alternatively, if you find the list tedious and not beneficial perhaps it should be more granular and include tasks you really want to do, but feel you never get around to. The latter case can serve as a motivator to complete those tasks while allowing you to visualize the blockers that keep you from accomplishing them.

Lists can be physical or virtual, whatever works best for you. I prefer to handwrite mine giving each a unique, visual aspect, square boxes for must do's, and circles for optional's, etc. (see the figure below for an example). In my experience, the optimal size for a list is no more than 5-8 tasks, beyond that can be stressful and you may end up dividing your attention and not getting everything done.

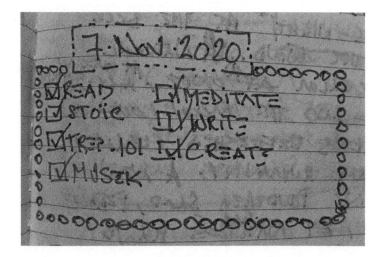

Figure 1: Handwritten To-Do List

Now my lists won't mean much to you, as they're written for my eyes only and for me to understand. Several items on those lists are habits rather than tasks. In this case I use the list and the physical act of checking it off as a method of keeping my 'streak' going. Both the

Stoic philosophers and comedian and sitcom star, Jerry Seinfeld, have some great advice on streaks – using them for building good habits or removing bad ones. Google "Seinfeld Chain" or "Seinfeld Strategy" for the entire story but essentially he advises getting a calendar and marking off a day every time you do (or don't do) something in which you want to create a habit of, for him this is writing jokes. After some time, maybe a month or so, you'll have a streak going (30 days or greater), and the longer the streak becomes the more you want to keep at it and not "break the chain," which quickly becomes a real motivational strategy.

I draw my checklist for the following day sometime the evening before, usually during my nightly review of tomorrow's schedule. On my present 8-item list, 6 of them are things I do every day without fail, a smaller subset of those (3-4) I have done every single day without missing a beat for over three years; sometimes performing the tasks on airplanes, trains, or remote parts of the Colombian jungle with no phone or Internet. Some items on the list take as little as 2 minutes while others can more than 2 hours, but this is the style of list that I've adapted and works for me. Over the last few years I've completed every single item on my list over 95% of the time and all optional activities more than 85%. That alone serves a evidence justifying the amazing productivity tool that list-making has become for me.

MAKING ADJUSTMENTS

No matter how well you've scheduled your day, how diligent your prep work the night before, or how adept you've become at completing every single task on your list – from time to time circumstances and forces beyond your control will rear their heads and derail your plans. That's life, and to quote the Stoics the only aspect of it within your complete control is your own mind – in everything else circumstances can intervene. We can prepare as much as possible but when something unexpected occurs or things go wrong there is no advantage in getting upset or angry. Instead we need to adapt and deal with the situation that has commandeered your attention. If you can alleviate the complication immediately, that's fantastic, but if not, develop a strategy to deal with it as best you can moving forward for the duration of the problem.

We don't need to delve every potential scenario that could arise, ranging from losing your job, a flat tire on your car, a sick child, or a global pandemic locking the world down – you get the idea. The key is to try to keep your cool (don't fret if you don't, most of us aren't zen masters), and regain control of the situation. Step back and logically assess what you need to do to a) rearrange your day (e.g., cancel/shift appointments, realistically determine what can be completed today vs what has to be shelved etc.), and b) develop a strategy or base framework to navigate the new and unexpected situation. In the case of a sick child you'll have to cancel or move any appointments which you'll be unable to attend while collecting the child, hopefully you can salvage some of those via telephone or video conference and plan the remainder of your day to work from your home whilst caring for the child.

SUMMARY

Developing a process that works for you is integral, not only to your time but to maximize your individual performance. If you're constantly stretched, juggling tasks and leaving important initiatives unfinished there's no chance you'll be able to be your best self. I've provided you with the templates from which you can draw, bend and shape as fits and works for you. Once you find the sweet spot, work within it and remember it's not fixed or a cage. You can and should continue to reassess and tweak the process as your life changes and as you become more attuned to what works for you.

Unexpected things *will* come up, someone will throw a wrench into your gears, but you need a process (and a form of resilience and continuity planning therein) to deal with those issues when they occur. Such events should be rarities and if you find the same things occurring time and again, that should inform your process that it needs to adapt to accommodate that problem or leave allotted space and time to deal with it as a regular occurrence.

CHAPTER SIX

WALKING

"All truly great thoughts are conceived while walking."
– FRIEDRICH NIETZSCHE, TWILIGHT OF IDOLS.

This book has a chapter dedicated to Physical Exercise, so why the focus on walking? While I wholeheartedly agree that walking is a form of exercise, if you've already had a look at the Physical Exercise section and the intensity level of the activities therein, mountaineering-style trail hikes and treks notwithstanding, the difference is apparent. The type of walking addressed in this chapter focuses on mind rather than body though of course it benefits both.

Many individuals now lauded for their creative and world-changing ideas or works of art made a habit of long daily walks. Charles Darwin had his 'thinking path,' Nietzsche, Goethe, Albert Einstein, Nikola Tesla, Immanuel Kant and a great many other notable figures made walking an important part of both their day and creative process. A 2014 Stanford University study found walking can boost creativity by 60-81% with effects remaining after the walk as well.

If you have a choice, opt for nature over a city walk, a nearby park is a great option. But if you've been relegated to a city walk that works too, you simply need to ensure you make the best of it. Trees, grass, and greenery all help to strengthen our minds and bodies harkening back to a time when we all lived in natural surroundings. Nature produces an abundance of negative ions which are plentiful in the sun's UV rays (along with your needed dose of vitamin D), colliding water (e.g., waterfalls, shorelines, beaches), and created during the growth cycle of plants. Being outside and in the wilds of nature is another pillar in the tower of health and performance you're building and just like exercise, diet, and sleep, it's not something you should neglect.

The positive effects of negative ions (negative ionization) include: boosting your immune system, improving cognitive function and memory, reducing stress, assisting sleep regulation, and enhancing your mood. Think back to the last time you walked along a beach or explored a waterfall – it's difficult to imagine being in a bad mood when doing so. There's evidence showing negative ions can inhibit and kill harmful bacteria, viruses, and molds, something noted during the recent COVID-19 pandemic.

Like many people I find I think better, with enhanced clarity and creativity, and further 'outside of the box' – drawing connections between previously unconsidered ideas when outdoors and otherwise engaged. I'm not the only one who feels this way, there are numerous studies examining the effects of walking on cognition and thinking patterns, and just as many theories and explanations as to why walking affects us as it does (i.e., increased blood flow and oxygen to the brain, activating the hippocampus, the step rhythm influencing thinking, etc.).

Walking is a great way to spend time with others and socialize away from the relentless media barrage, work distractions, and your ever-present devices (hopefully you abstain from using them when walking). Walking encourages you to live in the moment resulting in more conversations of greater depth and meaning which strengthens relationships and can lead to new and fresh ideas.

Finally, there's no better way to explore, get to know your surroundings and discover paths and places untrodden. We evolved over thousands of years to walk. It's the most natural way for humans to navigate the world around them and there's certainly a host of other benefits and reasons that it makes us feel good we've yet to dissect and uncover on a scientific level. With that in mind and in the spirit of exploration and discovery, why not get out and walk?

THE METHOD

There are a few specific techniques I'd suggest incorporating into your walks, methods that allow for maximum benefit. I'll start with one which I expect to get some pushback – **don't wear headphones or earphones**. There are plenty of times when listening to music, a podcast, or an audiobook is great, but for this kind of walk they're unnecessary distractions. Part of the point is to be in the moment, focused on your environment, your surroundings, and potentially any other people or happenstance interactions. Note the squirrels chasing one another, ducks in the pond, birds chirping. Allow yourself to be immersed in your environment and distracted by *it*, not by some pre-programmed aspect of the attention-seeking economy. To help resist temptation, make it easy on yourself and leave your headphones (or device) at home, and please don't be one of those people who plays your phone at full volume outside while walking around.

The next aspect is *enabled or encouraged* by your headphone-free walk – engaging with your community. You know those movies and TV shows filled with quaint scenes of characters walking out of their homes or around the neighborhood smiling at people, greeting them, even engaging in idle chit-chat with strangers. Imagine that – looking into the eyes of someone you don't or barely know, without doing a commercial transaction or having any agenda whatsoever. All easy to avoid when we walk around in curated bubbles, headphones plugged in, tuned out the world around us in favor of the pre-programmed world inside. I'm not completely bashing this – there's a time and place for both, but I do mean both, you need to engage and open yourself to surprise, ideas, and opportunities. It's amazing how much more at home you feel in your community when you start recognizing people and putting names to faces. You never know who or what kind of people you may meet, what kind of interaction you may have that spurs new ideas, ways of thinking, or inspiring and pushing you in a completely different direction. I guarantee you're more likely to have an occurrence such as this or a happenstance interaction when not wrapped in the curated world of your headphones.

The only allowance I give for using a smart device during walks (beyond navigation), is for capturing ideas and inspirations all around you. This doesn't mean taking a video or picture every five minutes of your journey (please don't), but if there's something truly remarkable and special you'll know it. The main thing I use my phone for when walking is jotting down notes and ideas (using whatever your favorite note-taking app may be), which could just as easily be done carrying a notepad and pencil.

CITY WALKS

A final note on city walks and walking – owed some love after making the case for nature walking above. Over the course of one's life there are bound to be days, times and places when those nature walks just aren't an option. Lucky for you walking is far and away the best way to see a city, be it the one you live in or a place you're visiting. You're bound to discover alternate routes, intriguing cafes and restaurants off the beaten path and beyond the tourist guides.

SUMMARY

Beyond Nietzsche and his chapter opening quote, the amount of crossover between individuals who've made great leaps of knowledge and invention alongside being habitual walkers is a crowded space. Aristotle was rumored to have taken his students on walks to while teaching. Steve Jobs liked to walk during meetings, claiming it allowed him to focus on the content of the discussion rather than office distractions. Charles Dickens was well known for daily walks of up to 20 or 30 miles in and around London during which he'd map out ideas and characters based on the people and things encountered along the way. Famed composers Pyotr Tchaikovsky and Ludwig Von Beethoven walked habitually taking inspiration from the countryside and woodlands surrounding them. Beethoven even carried paper and a writing implement with him, composing his nature-inspired Sixth Symphony, the 'Pastoral Symphony,' on walks such as these.

You're in good company by walking regularly and to give Pascal's Wager another angle – what do you have to lose by doing so?

Stepping away from distraction, getting outside and into nature is never a bad bet for relieving stress, elevating mood, and coming up with ideas and solutions.

If it wasn't for reading neither of us would be here communing across time and space via this medium. By now you will have noticed a consistent pattern throughout this book, ties that bind everything together – First are the methods, adjustments, or processes that help to feel better, be healthier, and enhance performance. Second, each and every one of these methods have a long history of working for humanity. They are not crazy, new, or trendy notions – though some may appear to be – instead they go back centuries, if not tens of thousands or millions of years. Many of them are a part of our wild nature and while I won't argue that reading is part of our nature, it is something that has been around for a long while and has helped us both as individuals and as a society to communicate across cultures, geographies, and eras. The written word and reading itself has enabled us to make leaps and bounds forward in progress and in evolving both our internal and external structures.

Reading can be done virtually anywhere, anytime, and modern technology has helped further the accessibility and content delivery while reducing the medium's ecological footprint. For my money, there's no better or more reliable method of gaining new insights and ideas than delving into a book. Beyond that reading has a lighter and simpler pleasure – fun. Books have been around for a long time and compared to the relative lifespan of a human, they're almost infinite. This means no matter who you are you're sure to find books that speak to your mind, body, heart and soul. Mysteries, business strategy, self-improvement, geopolitics, odes & epics, philosophy, poetry, graphic novels and comic books, math and scientific texts, are just some of the limitless categories you can delve into. The best part is you don't have to choose just one, instead you can flip and bounce between any and all subjects and genres offered up, opening worlds and creating new connections in your mind along the way.

METHODS

What you choose to read, your style, and method of consumption is highly subjective but I'll mention a few pointers and ideas that have worked for me. My first suggestion may be controversial and I'm unaware of any scientific studies on the subject, but it's something I've found useful and you've nothing to lose by giving it a try.

Read Multiple Books at Once

It complicates the answer to the common question "What are you reading?" but besides that small inconvenience I've found this vastly improves my reading output as well as overall cognitive function. When you think about it, it's no more difficult that maintaining a few ongoing conversations via email or text, as we all do. You may ask – Why? Well, why not? I expect the list of books you'd like to read is more than a single book, so why not tackle a few at once? In my experience, there's ways to do this well and ways that don't work as well. For example, I wouldn't recommend reading two novels at once, particularly two books from the same series or by the same author. Instead, spread both the subject matter and genres around to help your mind easily separate the content and storylines. I read 3-5 books at at time but never will I be reading 2 novels at once. My current reading list contains 4 books (and my aforementioned daily mini-dose of Stoic or other philosophical material post-meditation): A mystery novel, a biography, a poetry collection, and a book on evolution and genetics. At a glance there's not a lot of overlap or confusion between the content therein, so the likelihood of confusion is slim. Of course there's always a chance for some cross-over but that's a happy coincidence – a little piece of serendipity to make you wonder about the strange and mystical workings of the universe.

Advantages of reading multiple books simultaneously:

- Balance books you're required to read for work or school vs. books to relax and enjoy.

- Allow yourself space to stretch outside of your standard reading comfort zone, delving into a subject or style you know little to nothing about can lead to new perspectives.

- Lighten the load of a large tome you're trudging through by reading several smaller or lighter books alongside it.

- It can alleviate the pressure of "sunk cost," that in which you continue throwing valuable resources (in this case, your time) into something which is not giving you worthwhile return for your efforts, i.e. a book you simply do not like or enjoy. In such a case I suggest the 10% rule as a standard guideline, if you're 10% into a book and not enjoying it or learning anything – stop reading it. You don't have time to waste reading books you don't enjoy when there's so many out there that you will.

E-Readers vs. Classic Books

A thoroughly modern debate – which to choose and why? This is down to personal preference but I'll share a few thoughts and experiences I've had with both. Initially I was very reluctant to give up physical, paper books. As a stalwart fan of the classic book making the switch to an E-Reader was difficult. I estimate it took me six months to a year of concentrated effort to really get into it and I still have some gripes which I'll delve into later in this section.

I now read most of my books in electronic format. E-Readers have a lot of advantages that I've come to appreciate and while I'm in no way a 'power user', these are some of the basic benefits any reader will approve of:

You can carry thousands of books in your pocket. It's much easier to carry and read multiple books on an E-Reader than to lug around a bunch of 1000-page tomes.

Modern devices have warm, non-blue light-emitting backlights. This means you can read in low-light situations without the need for an external light, and potentially disturbing anyone who may be trying to sleep beside you.

- You can highlight sections and passages with a swipe of the finger. Making them easy to reference later be it for research, self-interest, or to share them with friends.

- When you don't know or understand a word, you simply press on it and are instantly transported to a dictionary definition and/or a Wikipedia article (provided you have an Internet connection).

- Digital books tend to be significantly cheaper than paper books.

- And of course, they're better for the environment.

- You can sync your E-Reader book with the Audiobook version allowing you to easily switch between reading and listening formats.

I have no doubt there's dozens more, but as mentioned I'm no power user and in no way am I trying to push my own preferences or promote the sale of such devices – how you choose to consume your books is up to you. On the flipside of the argument there's several aspects of E-Readers that I dislike and as far as the technology goes, there's a lot of room for improvement. Some negatives:

- They do not replicate the feel of a classic book.

- If the book you're reading has a lot of imagery or graphical content (i.e. graphic novels, comic books, certain types of scientific literature, etc.), they're just plain awful and don't compare to a physical book, particularly if the images are intricate and in-color.

- You can't pick up a book and just flip to a random page in search of an idea, inspiration or chance quote.

• Finally, from time to time it's difficult recalling the title and author of the book you're reading because you don't see the cover every time you pick it up to read.

Audiobooks

As a child, I had a good collection of books on record. Condensed, Coles notes-style versions of fairytales, movies, or other stories, that included a picture book to follow along with the story. There would be a chime or sound on the record alerting you when it was time to turn the page. Adult books were also available on record and as technology progressed from record to cassette to compact disc the act of listening to books became easier. You could have an entire novel on a single disc with the chapters delineated by track making it relatively simple to just sit back and listen.

The audiobook has taken huge strides enabled by the modern age of streaming media along with the capability to store vast amounts of data on small portable devices. While I'm aware of several audiobook delivery platforms this section focuses on Audible.com; not as an endorsement but solely because it's the service I use and am most familiar with. I expect most platforms offer similar capabilities and this section primarily focuses on the delivery method itself.

The ease and accessibility of audiobooks (most services are available via a low-cost monthly subscription) is a great way to increase your book consumption with minimal effort. How much content you actually retain and get out of audiobooks is subjective and dependent upon a combination of your style of learning as well as the environment you're listening in. I supplement my reading by no more than one audiobook at a time. I do think it's good to have a mix of consumption methods but tend to use the old school reading method for the bulk of my books and select specific titles to consume audibly. There are a few benefits of audiobooks which I enjoy, namely, the capability of adjusting the playback speed. The service I use allows you to do this on a very granular scale, currently ranging from 0.1x all the way through 3.5x narration speed. This is a great tool, allowing you to finish a book slated for 9-hours in a 6-hour window if listening at 1.5x speed. The capability of syncing your audiobook with your E-Reader enables you to read on the go, allowing you to read at home or while commuting by train, and listen when driving or cooking dinner.

When selecting books to *listen* to, there are certain criteria to look for:

- Who's narrating the book? Books narrated by the Author or containing an interesting cast of narrators tailored to the story or book-type tend to be best.

- The length of the book being read. While some people may easily consume a 40-hour audiobook, my maximum duration is around 15 hours or so.

- The type of book itself – If it's a complex subject or an intricate, multilayered story with multiple sections and characters, it can be difficult to consume as an audiobook, the opportunity for distraction is simply too great. Sure you can rewind, jump to specific chapters etc., but that quickly gets tedious and listening may end up taking more time than reading in the end.

SUMMARY

No matter what you're trying to achieve or improve it's hard to go wrong with reading books

- not news articles or blog posts. Too much of the latter is targeted to grab and retain your attention rather than provide you with real information and new points of view. The effort, diligence, dedication, and discipline required to write a book versus that of a magazine article or blog post differ by orders of magnitude. Not to disparage all such content, but your chances of striking gold and finding real inspiration or revelation in a book are far greater so you might as well play the odds. Everyone should have at least one book underway at any given time, it doesn't matter how fast or slow you read or how many books you read, what matters is that you're learning, increasing your own knowledge and expanding your mind. It's a much more productive and purposeful use of the short time we're allotted than mindlessly scrolling social media feeds – don't bother with that old "I don't have time excuse," stop cheating yourself and pick up a book.

CHAPTER EIGHT

WRITING

Our minds are in a constant state of activity, fluttering with thousands of ideas, worries, hopes, anxieties, to-do lists etc. Focus and flow are things we all strive to achieve regardless of different end goals or what we do on a day-to-day basis. There are many methods of bringing calm to the chaos and some sort of order to the haphazard thoughts vying for your attention; this book looks at several, including meditation and walking. This chapter, however, shines a light on my favorite technique, and one I use in multiple ways every single day.

Writing brings together a lot of the things I love – it makes me feel good simply in *the act of producing something*, regardless of the quality (which is often subjective). It helps to organize those scattered thoughts swirling about your head almost without even trying, you just sit down, write and let it flow. A favourite part of my day is when my partner and I sit across rom one another, writing side-by-side while sipping our morning coffee. It may take a few words, sentences, or paragraphs to get going but if you let your subconscious take over and keep that pen scribbling or keyboard clicking, you'll often surprise yourself with what comes out. Another benefit of daily writing is you generate a trail of thought and growth, perhaps even purpose and legacy. Of course you can also enjoy the ritual experience of burning or erasing writings, symbolizing rebirth or a new start, but in general, you're going to create a collection or archive of *something* which you can keep completely private or share with friends, children, or grandchildren even long after you're gone.

Before we delve into a few writing methods below, it's important to remember that whatever form of writing you choose or how many words or pages you commit to every day, consistency is key to achieving results.

METHODS & TOOLS

A recurring theme of the Savage Discipline is that the bulk of the methods described can be done almost anywhere for very little or no cost. This is both practical and lessens the impact of societal or economic stigma but also takes away your excuses. It's entirely up to you, your willpower, and your discipline to implement and adhere to what works for you.

What do you need to write? A pencil and paper, something a nameless large blue and yellow Swedish assemble-your-own-furniture store will be happy to provide, free-of-charge, should one be in your vicinity. It's entirely up to you which tools and implements you feel comfortable writing with. I alternate depending on what I'm doing and like anything else it's good to force yourself to adapt and switch-up those regular methods from time to time. There are a few basic tools to choose from:

- Pen, pencil, marker, crayon etc. and some form of paper, notebook, napkin etc.

- Computer or Laptop

- Tablet or Smartphone

- Typewriter or Word Processor

I won't get into methods of writing with a pen-like instrument and paper – that's been covered in detail by your parents and teachers. But I'll provide some tips and techniques for the other mediums mentioned.

If you use a digital device there are numerous free applications available and most common platforms include one or more free writing tools pre-installed. There's no reason to shell out hard earned cash on special designed writing software unless it's something you deem necessary to your workflow. If you're writing on a tablet or smartphone I'd recommend keeping it short & sweet or investing in an external keyboard of some sort to lessen the chances of developing some form of repetitive stress injury.

There are a lot of apps available for jotting down quick notes and ideas and all of those discussed here are free. Google Keep is my app of choice as it has a feature set that works for me: it's easily searchable, you can organize notes via colors, labels/tags, pin selected notes, archive notes, collaborate and share with contacts, export to Google Docs, include links and images etc. The best bit is that all of your notes are accessible and updated instantly on all of your devices. Many friends and colleagues swear by Evernote, Apple Notes, Dropbox Paper, or Microsoft OneNote, and I expect those apps all have similar capabilities to Google Keep functions already mentioned. Explore a few and try them out to find which best suits your style.

If you're writing longer musings, a story or book projects or you simply require more features, I'll again give the nod to Google and their free Google Docs app. This is still my preferred writing application, for a non-power user (like myself), it's got all the features of Microsoft Word and I don't have to pay a dime for it; and again I can access my content on any device. I have a habit of writing a song or a poem every day, usually by hand while sitting outside. I view this exercise as a draft and towards the end of the day I take five minutes to transpose it into a Google Doc, doing a first revision and cleaning it up somewhat while ensuring I have a digital copy to archive.

DAILY WRITINGS

These can be whatever you want them to be, but some form of daily writing practice is essential maintenance to declutter and sort out the constant stream of input your brain receives every day. Never before in human history have we been constantly bombarded with such a non-stop onslaught of media, ideas, or communications. It's an all-out assault on the psyche from the moment you wake until you fall asleep; it's little wonder psychological disorders and insomnia are more prevalent than ever. Having a form of automated, daily writing is a great avenue to help your mind get things out in the open and sort through them. Again, it doesn't have to be something you really think about, rather it's the process of putting pen to paper or fingers to keyboard and seeing (or ignoring) what comes out.

There are people who write three words every day in the form of things they're thankful or grateful for. Others like to jot down details of their day, things they did, or how they felt at certain times. Still others might want to write down goals, ideas, or strategies. The point is there are no rules here, it doesn't matter, you can do either or none of those or switch between them each and every day. But the act of downloading something from your mind to a page will help your conscious and subconscious mind to structure things a little differently perhaps revealing solutions that had previously escaped you. It shouldn't take a lot of time out of your day and if you find it doing so try setting a time or word limit.

A few ideas to get started:

- Journaling / Chronicling your day

- Ideas (business, wants, desires, new habits etc.)

- Freeform – just throw words together as you feel and see what comes out

- Drawing – while not technically 'writing' this counts and works just as well

- Gratitudes / Things to be thankful for

- Dreams – dream journal or log

- Affirmations / Goals

- Poems

SCATTERED CREATION

A method of writing I use almost every day is what I call 'makeshift' or 'scattered' creation. Not to be confused with the cut-up methodology attributed to Brion Gysin and William S. Burroughs (also worth looking into).

In scattered creation, one searches for a jumping off point which can literally come from anything and everything. Common jumping off points I use are random phrases or word I like the sound of, a picture or a painting, a childhood memory, an interaction at work, a TV series or film, a conversation fragment – hopefully you get the point, again, there are no rules, this can be anything.

From that starting point I then do some freeform association around the word or words, again without rules – it can be words or sentences that come into my mind based on that starting point, it can be words that rhyme with it, synonyms, antonyms etc. Anything that comes into your flow, just get it all out. That's your initial scattering, a pool from which you can draw upon and this is where some similarity to the previously mentioned cut-up method could come into play.

With the fresh scattering, you've got a new jumping off point – a collection of words and phrases to work with and around, whether you are building a poem, a story, a character, a song, or whatever you intend to use it for. It's important to note your specific intent didn't have to be determined at the outset but you are now free to do with it what you will.

LONG-FORM

Two of the most common methods of long-form writing you hear about are: The Gardener or Farmer method, and the Architect or Framework method. There's another method which I sometimes use and have termed the Michelangelo method. I expect there's dozens more but these are the three I use and am most familiar with.

The Michelangelo Method

One of the greatest, if not *the greatest* Sculptor of all time, Michelangelo believed the stunning forms and scenes he brought forth from the marble were always there, simply encased in the stone. As an artist it was his duty to strip away the excess material and debris, releasing the intended forms into the world.

You can apply this method to writing by pulling words from a blank page. I wrote an entire novel using this method, laying down a rule that I'd have to write two-pages every day and stuck to it. I had no plan, no outline, no plot, no characters, nothing. I just sat down and released what was within the page every day. Eighty-three days later I had a draft of something. As to how good it was, that's subjective, but it worked and I created something by pulling words from the page.

The Gardener / The Farmer

Just as it sounds, the Gardener or Farmer plants seeds and watches them grow. With seeds you have some idea of what you may get or at least what you hope you to get but you don't know exactly what the final plant will look like or how the fruit will appear or taste – there's a lot of unknowns. You scatter some seeds to the wind and see which ones take root, germinate and grow to fruition.

The Architect / Frameworks

Before attempting to write anything long-form I'd always assumed this was how it worked. Everything mapped out and framed into scenes, cue cards, lines drawn between relationships, detailed character sketches etc. The foundational prep work required to 'build' a book. Only after the foundation was laid could the writer begin tying all these aspects together into a flowing, creative, and beautifully structured narrative.

In this method you are architecting the story, building it up piece by piece and then putting it all together. To date, this book is the closest I'd adhered to that structural format. I dreamed of a few chapters and jotted down outlines for them. The following morning I sat down and sketched out every chapter, adding some new ones and some point-form notes detailing what I wanted to include in each section. When I really got down to the business of writing, I set myself a minimum word limit and simply went about filling in the chapters.

As you've gathered, you don't have to dogmatically stick to one of the above methods or any others out there. You can instead weave in and out utilizing different methods for different parts of your work, using whatever serves best to get the job done.

EDITING

Editing is difficult but essential if you intend to publish or show your work to anyone. There's no skirting around it, it must be done. I am a terrible editor, particularly concerning my own work. I get caught in endless cycles mulling over too many options and ideas, ending up with a cluttered mess of comments, sticky notes, and alternate versions of songs, poems, stories, that I don't know what to do with or where to begin. There's an inherent fear in either throwing away something valuable, having it die a lonely death on the cutting room floor, or worse, not producing the best possible version of the work you can.

Of course, all of that is ridiculous, what may be the best version to one reader may be the worst to another and vice-versa. As such, you need to choose your reviewers, ideal readers, and editors (be they the same or different individuals) carefully. You want to trust them, their guidance, and opinions to steer you and your work in the right direction, making it better than it was. You'll notice a lot of writers, filmmakers, and musicians stick with the same editors (or producers in the case of music), throughout their careers or at least phases of them, and for good reason; editing is an art in and of itself, and when you're handing over the raw materials you've labored so hard to unearth the last thing you want is to get them back in worse shape than they were originally.

You want your editors to understand your vision and audience, if not share it. They need to understand you, or this part of you, and what you're striving to build. A great editor will go beyond things such as grammar, punctuation, and formatting. They'll give you ideas and direction on areas to expand and (the painful part) complete sections to cut because they are simply not serving your purpose, something that can be very difficult to see when you're the creator.

If you're like me and produce a lot of material in different and varied areas (songs, fiction, non-fiction, poems etc.), you may want to seek out and construct different teams or groups of reviewers who understand what you're going for within each area or genre you're working.

There are a few rules I use for editing written work. It's a good idea to experiment with several methods to see how your results differ. The general process I use follows the steps below:

1. Upon completing the work, **shelve it and let it marinate or ferment**. Like you're making pickles or aging cheese. You need to get yourself and your mind away from this thing

that you've been focusing on day in and day out for weeks or months at a stretch. You need to forget it and come back with fresh eyes and a clean perspective. The duration of the aging is subjective, but for me it depends on both the total length of the piece itself as well as the amount of time spent toiling over it. On the quick end, for a short piece, e.g. a sub-2000 word short story, I recommend a minimum of 2 weeks. For a novel or larger project you need 4-6 weeks. During that fermentation period you shouldn't be thinking about the work at all, let alone looking at it. You should have your mind on something else, start a new project, take a vacation, do whatever, just don't focus on the work.

2. After aging to a good level of ripeness, you can revisit the work and be delighted and horrified accordingly (probably both), as you go through it word by word, page by page, fixing the obvious errors, ensuring the story flows and makes sense as you and your subconscious envisioned. It's when you've completed this stage and decided you're happy with the work and don't need to do a complete rewrite, overhaul or scrap it (yes, we all know that pain, and unfortunately it will happen from time to time), then you have your first sharable draft.

3. You're now ready to release those raw diamonds to the small army of reviewers, ideal readers and editors that you've assembled. Incorporating their feedback, critiques and suggestions as you see fit (you're still the director here) and polishing your product.

SUMMARY

Writing doesn't have to be work. You don't have to aspire to be a Nobel laureate or write an epic ode that sets the world on fire. It doesn't even have to be shared. It's simply another tool to work out your thoughts, problems, and ideas. Chances are you already do this in different forms, be it talking to a trusted friend, advisor, or bartender. It's natural for humans to fall into habits that help them cope with their lives – the trickier part is pivoting from these routines and trying new methods and ways to come up with solutions and ideas. Adaptation and flexibility are keys to keeping both your mind and body fresh as well as continually developing and learning.

And if you do want to be a prize-winning novelist or set the world on fire with a poem or new philosophy, what's holding you back? Creativity and ideas aren't hallowed ground where only private and vetted members are admitted. One of our strongest and most compelling features as a species is how we attack problems and come up with creative solutions and ideas. This is in your blood; all you need to do is borrow a pencil and some scrap paper and start writing.

CHAPTER NINE

LIMITATIONS & RESTRICTIONS

"To know thyself is the beginning of wisdom"

– SOCRATES.

Much of the western world has enjoyed an unprecedented standard of living over the past few centuries. While it's easy to complain about how such and such isn't working or how terrible a certain politician or political system may be, we often forget how lucky and privileged we are to live as we do and how much less most people subsist on. I'm not saying we should become complacent but it is important to maintain perspective and appreciate that many of us live in an affluent society that provides social services and safety nets that the rest of the world would give an arm and a leg to have.

The years when I spent in the post-war Balkan nations of Bosnia & Herzegovina and Kosovo, along with a half-decade traveling the ruggedly beautiful and diverse yet struggling Afghanistan enriched my life in ways that will resonate forever. Like anyone else I get frustrated with silly things such as my Internet not working but when I step back and visualize the bigger picture and how small a piece of it we are, I am in awe of the endless possibilities and unknowns. Not to mention how brief, fragile and delicate life is – reminding me to make the most of it and my short time here.

Many of us have grown accustomed to living by excuses as to why we can't or aren't doing something, or justifying why we'll put it off until later – the tomorrow that never comes.

Besides the dreaded "I don't have time" justification, other frequent culprits include not having such-and-such an item or being able to buy some absolute must have piece of equipment or tool. The most productive people are the ones who don't make excuses instead they make do with what they have and get on with it. The end result may not be perfect or may not be like so-and-so's, but it will be your own and completed, as the famous Silicon Valley saying goes, "Done is better than perfect." Once the first draft or version of something is complete there's no reason you can't do further iterations to improve upon it or take those learnings and apply them towards a better resourced next effort. The only person you're putting off by making excuses is yourself and your own capabilities.

On the flip side of the coin we have a new issue. The affluence and opportunity prevalent in modern society coupled with the sinking cost of projects and production due to online and outsourced services and the still ongoing non-stop battle for our attention, results in a new challenge – We are overwhelmed with choice resulting in decision paralysis.

The oft-repeated Socrates quote that opens this chapter speaks of 'knowing thyself.' When you know yourself you are not only aware of your strengths but also your weaknesses and bad habits. Once identified you can use the power of limitations and restrictions to impede those negative tendencies. For example, I don't have a television. While I do watch some movies and shows it's very few and all on a small eleven-inch laptop screen. Limiting the medium ensures I don't get sucked in or waste too much time 'binging' or watching nonsense. It's a self-imposed limitation used to my advantage, enabling me to be more productive and make better use of my time.

Limitations can force you to adapt and create unique or better work by forcing you to discover new methods and ways of thinking. Below are a few famous examples of individuals harnessing the power of limitations and restrictions, using them as tools to accomplish tasks instead of excuses as to why they didn't.

DR. SEUSS

Dr. Seuss' books are among my childhood favorites. Their popularity has ensued, due to their completely unique works of art combining fantastical illustration along with clever, rhyming, rhythmic storytelling. Two of Seuss' most famous books, "The Cat in The Hat," and "Green Eggs and Ham" both came to fruition as a result of placing restrictions on himself. The former uses a total of 236 words, while the later has an amazing 50-word limit. Rumor has it that Seuss placed a bet with his publisher, claiming he could create books within such extreme limits. The publisher took the bet and lost – although how much he lost in the end is up for debate considering the continuing success of both titles.

KEITH JARRETT

Keith Jarrett is one of the greatest piano players alive. Regardless of taste even the most ardent naysayer would be hard pressed to disagree that he's one of the most talented improvisers we've seen in the last century. Jarrett is famous for playing wholly improvised concerts to sold out theatres – imagine, you have nothing planned, no script, no setlist, not even a song. Yet you have to walk on stage and perform creating everything on the spot for an audience of thousands who've paid upwards of a few hundred dollars a seat to see you.

It's not an easy ask. Few can do it and being one of the best is why Jarrett is such a draw. People want a glimpse of the divine, to watch inspired creation happen in the moment of inception. To help prepare Jarrett is known to have very strict requirements (restrictions!) for his concerts – No talking during the performance, and of course, not just any old piano will do, his rider details an instrument tailored to his exacting specifications. Without these things Mr. Jarrett will not play the show.

As discussed in Day & Scheduling, things don't always go as planned, and just like the rest of us Keith Jarrett sometimes has to adapt. In early 1975 a young promoter booked Jarrett to play a concert in Köln, Germany. Being a huge fan she did her best to follow the rider specifics and ordered a piano to meet his requirements but something went wrong and a small, beat up and out-of-tune baby grand was delivered by mistake. The pedals weren't working and the tone and timbre of the instrument were in no way apt for a concert hall performance let alone meet with Jarrett's standards.

To make matters worse, Jarrett had been having extremely painful back problems, interfering with his sleep and requiring that he wear a back brace. These factors combined with the poor instrument quality forced Keith and his manager to cancel the performance. Keith had gotten into his vehicle and was preparing to depart when the young promoter came out of the venue begging him to reconsider.

No one other than Keith Jarrett himself can say what caused the change of heart, but he did, and almost fifty years later the world was better for it. The resulting performance and recording issued afterward were stunning. Due to the limitations of the instruments as well as his own physical restrictions Jarrett was forced to adapt his style, focusing on the mid-range of the piano and playing a variety of hypnotic and astonishing rhythms and melodies drawing from numerous musical forms.

The performance was recorded and the resulting album, known simply as "The Köln Concert" ended up being both the best-selling solo album in jazz and best-selling piano album in history.

SUMMARY

When I think of the power of limitations and restrictions a lot of musical acts spring to mind, from The White Stripes, to Django Reinhardt, to the very creation of venerable forms such as blues and hip hop. Art and design have entire movements dedicated to minimalism and restriction. The Danish Dogma 95 filmmaking adherents revel in restriction, as did Alfred Hitchcock's "Rope" – the entire film being one long single scene. The beautiful and creative designs utilized in the modern 'small house' movement were created as a direct result of increasing costs and unaffordability of housing in many parts of the world.

Limitations and restrictions can make you feel like an underdog. They give you something you're forced to push through or work around and upon doing so you're rewarded with a feeling of overcoming adversity – a huge motivator in itself. It also encourages you to think creatively, hack the system, and think outside the box, coming up with new methods and processes for achieving what you need to do. Use limitations and restrictions to your advantage, harness them as tools to develop new and inventive ways to deal with situations, solve problems, and create.

CHAPTER TEN

LISTENING & SPEAKING

> "To the youngster talking nonsense Zeno said, 'The reason why we have two ears and only one mouth is so we might listen more and talk less.'"

The title of this chapter is purposefully arranged so that 'Listening' is placed before 'Speaking.' Have you ever been to a meeting that turned into a game show with every attendee hurrying to shout their point of view before time runs out? Such situations amount to posturing contests, usually at the expense of results or actions accomplished. I know I have, and sometimes this can seem to be all that meetings are about. Has anyone ever cut you off or spoken over you, disregarding what you were saying and derailing your train of thought?

Perhaps you've been one of the perpetrators in either of the above scenarios. Again, I know I have.

Human communication can be difficult, particularly in certain environments and a society where we're doling out micro-doses of attention to hundreds if not thousands of different tasks and entities throughout the day. In a world where we are constantly assailed with media and messages begging us for actions and reactions it is increasingly difficult to take a breath, slow down, focus and *really listen*. You could be missing out on so much, a deeper connection and understanding, a fantastic idea or inspiring jumping off point, all because we're losing the battle to tame our brains and focus.

We sell ourselves short every time this happens, not only because we might miss something but also because yet again our attention has been stolen. Our wandering mind defeats us and keeps us from learning from others and doing our own best work. Studies show that the human brain is not built for multitasking, most of us cannot do it. This is a battle between those who want to wear down your resilience and steal your focus for their profit, and yourself and the way in which you were built to operate and perform at your best.

On those times when you're able to stop and catch yourself from speaking first or over someone you notice a few things occur depending upon the situation. During meetings when one of the group isn't attempting to shout and speak up over everyone you'll find people actually tend to pause and check themselves a little more when that individual chooses to speak. As you sit and listen, more often than not others will *ask* for your thoughts and opinions on the subject at hand. Once asked, you have the floor and from that platform others in the group will to listen and engage more as well.

In less formal settings or one-on-one scenarios, you'll watch your stature and level of respect rise within the group. Instead of being yet another constantly flapping jaw (that too often says nothing), you'll be the person who listens, gains trust, reliability, and is counted on to provide thoughtful advice. In one-on-one scenarios your friends and relations will appreciate speaking to someone who actually listens instead of waiting for their chance to respond or even to solve the issues they may be discussing, sometimes people just want to be heard.

Contrary to instinct the less you speak the more you'll find people willing and curious to listen when you do. Hopefully, this is because when you do speak your words have some thought and poignancy behind them. You don't need to deliver a stunning speech or revelation every time you open your mouth, but having something to say instead of filling the silence with nonsense is noticed and goes a long way.

Speak clear, slow, and with purpose. People tend to speak fast because they believe this will make them appear more intelligent, giving the impression of having more to say and getting more content across just like the media. But the exact opposite is true. When someone is speaking carefully and slowly it lends conviction and a sense of gravitas to their words. We're naturally more inclined to pay attention and listen. You're not marketing something, you don't need flowery adjectives and adverbs, if you're concise and to the point your message will be easier to digest and more poignant.

SUMMARY

Robert Greene offers a succinct summary for this chapter in Law 4 of his famous 48 Laws of Power – "Always Say Less Than Necessary." From the moment we learn to speak the tongue and our voices become a means to communicate in hopes of getting what we want. This habit becomes a beast, as once something has been said and unleashed you cannot reel it back in. For most of us speaking is easy but mastery is shown by those who carefully select and sparingly use their words to convey a point.

The majority of the time you don't need to explain your ideas down to the minutia, many concepts are more readily absorbed when the listener has to work out aspects on their own. Sarcasm is an easy (and sometimes tempting) trap to fall into but it can readily be misconstrued. There may be a time and place for it but be careful in its use. Besides, the world we live in could use a little more sincerity and truth anyways. Smile, listen, learn, and speak only when necessary and in as few words as possible.

This book is loosely structured in two ways. First, in order which you may address these areas throughout a regular day (Morning gets us rolling, while Sleep puts us to bed). But it also lays down the foundational aspects which the following practices build upon. Again returning to the three-legged stool analogy, we are sturdy and reliable only with all three legs intact: **Sleep, Nutrition, and Exercise**. If one of these is neglected, your memory, awareness, and overall mental acuity will be degraded.

My resume could be shrunk down to five words: *Good memory, good situational awareness*. Take it with a pinch of salt but there is an element of truth in that description. I'm no memory expert nor one of those individuals who can memorize a deck of cards or Pi to the nth degree or other memory super feats – but I do have a good memory. Whether this is due to nature or nurture I can't be certain but I suspect there's an element of both and I can attest the more you use it, the better it gets. I don't neglect my memory or awareness and I rely upon and exercise both each and every day.

MEMORY

It's not difficult to see how important a role our memories play. Our clever devices may have taken much of the burden away from us in the form of daily scheduling and reminders. While those events may be mini-milestones in your day, there's a whole lot of your day that isn't programmed into your device – how to walk, ride your bike, or drive; muscle memory used for physical training; how to make your meals or where to get them; directions to and from work or the gym; the names of family, friends, colleagues, community members, and so on. Imagine how complicated our days would become if we had to be reminded or look up each and every one of those things.

Memory training is important, even the smallest things can go a long way in making a difference in relationships and navigating our way through life. The following example highlights a common situation that many have experienced from one side or the other.

The Social Event

When attending a social event someone approaches you and addresses you by name, perhaps even mentioning some benign anecdote about you, a preference, something about your family etc. (nothing creepy just genuine familiarity and engagement).

Panic and anxiety set in – You either don't remember this person at all or have some vague recollection of a meeting but you're embarrassed and because you can't remember their name. The interaction feels lopsided. Clearly *they* thought it worth the effort to remember *your* name and even something you'd spoken about. You're now in the awkward position of having to ask them for their name or a reintroduction.

Going beyond the initial discomfort you'll note how that individual impressed you and made you feel good – you were someone worth remembering regardless of how brief your last encounter may have been. As a result you'll be certain to give them your full focus and attention this time around as you definitely don't want a repeat of the situation.

This individual managed to remember a few small bits of information – your face, name, and maybe a random anecdote. Not a lot of detail but it doesn't take much. You were caught off-guard and put onto your heels, increasing their stature and putting them in a position of power. Which side of this situation would you rather be on?

Training Your Memory

Anyone can troll through pages returned by a search engine or wiki page (though the accuracy of such information it up for debate), but recalling useful tidbits, facts and figures off the top of your head is more impressive and chances are you'll also be able to speak with more authority and conviction than something dredged up as the result of a quick web search. Such efforts will discipline your mind, training it to file and retrieve information and making new connections in ways beyond any search engine or algorithm in existence. Perhaps the largest incentive for training your memory instead of resorting to notes or electronic means is that the more you use it the better it works, the more you can learn, both of which help to protect the brain from deterioration.

Mnemonics is a general term used for systems and exercises to improve memory, the best of which go beyond that and help with overall mind function. Quick research on mnemonics reveals common ground shared with the Savage Discipline foundational aspects and other key methods we've touched upon; from physical exercise, to nutrition, to sleep, to walking. Each and every one is essential – but this section looks at some specific mental gymnastics which are fun challenges and have the added benefit of training you in patience and failure, both inevitable and difficult for us to swallow.

The best way to improve your memory is to grow your overall mental capacity and executive function, and the best way to do this is to learn new things and tackle tough problems, creating new neural pathways and synaptic connections in your brain. Try learning a new language, picking up a musical instrument you've never played before, teach yourself to draw or paint, join a debating club, a theatrical improv class, or enroll in an online course in programming, physics or chemistry. Anything completely new and outside of your comfort zone. It will be hard and frustrating; you might be terrible at it or the worst in the class, but the light at the end of the tunnel is that it **will** develop your mind. Besides, you probably won't be terrible for long due to the bell curve of learning; most of us tend to absorb the basics and general ideas of most things quickly – it's those rarified upper echelons of technique that separate masters from journeymen. This is evidenced when you examine the razor thin margins that determine the winners in professional-level competitions and sports.

That's the magic formula – go out and learn something completely new. There's a good chance you'll get frustrated and go far outside your comfort zone, but in the end, you'll have increased your mental capacity and memory, gaining a new skill or two along the way and feel great about it when all is said and done.

AWARENESS

An entire section focusing on Awareness is a product of the modern world and a key aspect I hope to address in this book. If we had a time machine and traveled back a millennium, even a century or two depending where you're located, there'd be little need to address such a faculty in ourselves – those lacking awareness would in all likelihood be dead. Imagine strolling through a forest or jungle unaware of the potential dangers and coming across some cute tiger or bear cubs at play only to have their mother show up and tear you to bits for threatening her progeny. In another situation, perhaps you inadvertently say something or make a benign gesture which causes grave offense, getting you thrown in jail or placed on the executioner's block. The savage ways of the world ensured we kept our wits about us or faced the consequences.

Awareness hasn't completely faded into obscurity, but it is fading fast. Sure, children are still taught to look both ways when they cross the road but we're on the way to ridding ourselves of that necessity too. We are trending towards a world where everyone is an island unto themselves, with technology enabling and strengthening those moats and walls every day.

The two kinds of awareness addressed here are intrinsically related: Self Awareness and Situational Awareness. More and more, we operate in bubbles of our own construction, enclosed in headphones and drawn into our devices; the world around us muted and blurred to minimize annoyance and ironically distraction. Returning to the time machine analogy, our time transporting human from a century ago visiting the present day would be aghast as they observed people talking and chuckling to themselves, ignoring others and the world around them while staring entranced into little boxes of plastic and metal. They would suspect the world had gone mad, all of us insane or possessed and ready for the sanitarium. If you stop for a minute to put down your device and take out your headphones is this what you'd call progress?

We are tribal creatures, that's how we're wired. Even as an introvert those same societal impulses are deeply ingrained. Introverts may have a heightened sense of awareness, wanting to avoid undue stress by stepping into a confrontation by not paying attention. Improving your situational awareness helps reduce the risk of the unexpected and keeps you safe. The earlier you become aware of a problem, be it something small or a potentially life-threatening situation, the more opportunity you have to take action and deal with it before it gets out of hand.

Self-awareness helps us operate and thrive in certain scenarios. While it's unlikely you'll find yourself amongst an unknown tribe, oblivious to their customs, offending their leader and being executed, you just may cost yourself a major deal or contract by blowing your nose in public in the wrong place. Self-awareness is a basic building block to making yourself better, finding areas of weakness so you can address and improve them, feel better about yourself, and increase your future performance. When you are self-aware you can act to prevent yourself from making harmful or detrimental mistakes.

When I become aware of a bad habit or tendency a technique I often use is to remove the option and make it difficult for myself to indulge the habit. For example, if I'm watching too much television, I get rid of the unit itself or cancel my streaming or cable subscription. Are you eating too much of a specific junk food? Stop purchasing that food or even going to the store where it's sold. Both subtle shifts make it easier to resist temptation and throw up barriers which make you think twice about the effort required for something you don't want to be doing anyways. On the other hand, if there's something you're not doing as often as you like, try to make it easy to accomplish some part of it rather than nothing. Want to start flossing your teeth daily? Commit to flossing one tooth a day. Start small and build on your successes.

Ernest Hemingway is one of my favorite authors, frequently mentioned in the amongst the greats and a Nobel-prize recipient. Even Hemingway was subject to bad habits, difficulties in getting his work done, and writers block – but he recognized these issues and implemented several methods to address them.

- He fastidiously tracked his daily written word output via charts, "so as not to kid myself." Holding his feet to the fire and refusing to fool himself. Hemingway knew when he was being productive and when he wasn't, there was no hiding from it.

- His next trick, presumably to address bouts of writer's block, was to "write one true sentence." Beginning can often be the most difficult part of any process and Hemingway recognized this. He'd sit down and force himself to start – to write the "truest sentence he knew," and then let the rest of the words flow.

In the same spirit there's a lot of things I choose to do and not to do, in keeping myself as healthy and productive as possible. I choose not to have a television because it greatly reduces the likelihood of wasting time watching it. I always keep my phone on silent – I don't need yet another aspect drawing my attention towards it. I keep the dental floss right beside my toothbrush so it's always on-hand to floss after brushing. You need to constantly assess yourself and your routine, calling out aspects needing improvment but also celebrating the wins. Learn from both failure and success, define strategies to address those areas in need of improvement via the removal or addition of something.

SUMMARY

Take a moment to consider some professions that interest you and the type of individuals who perform them; particularly that sense of awe in how one accomplishes such feats. Next, imagine how far you might be able to progress in those careers yourself if you had perfect recall and situational awareness. Depending on the types of professions you've dreamt up and assuming you're physically capable of performing the requisite skills, chances are you could get a good 80% of the way there with the proper application of your flawless memory and awareness. You'd only have to learn each skill or aspect a single time and to quickly understand the elements involved and how to navigate situations that arose. The remaining percentage is where your discipline and hard work come in – practicing complex tasks and honing them to perfection, learning from your mistakes (awareness), addressing and refining them. It's curious how rare the traits discussed in this chapter are mentioned in job advertisements or requirements when you realize how powerful the combination is and how far they can take you.

CHAPTER TWELVE

LEARNING & CREATION

"Inspiration is for amateurs. The rest of us just show up and get to work. If you wait around for the clouds to part and a bolt of lightning to strike you in the brain, you are not going to make an awful lot of work. All the best ideas come out of the process; they come out of the work itself."

– CHUCK CLOSE.

Learning and creation are forever entwined and difficult to envision as separate entities, they are reliant upon one another right down to the science of new neural pathways being *created* in your mind as you *learn* new things. Pure creation is the act of stringing together a bunch of random things you've learned in new ways, even human creation does this by entwining pieces of existing DNA to create a new individual.

Interesting things happen as you age – first of all, time goes faster as you experience more of it. When you were a year old, a single year took your entire life but by the time you're fifty it dwindles to a fiftieth, not so much. Similarly, when your mind is the blank slate of Plato's tabula rasa it is like a sponge ready to absorb anything and everything. When you know absolutely nothing about a subject you can exponentially increase your expertise by learning just a little. However, once you reach the peak of an 'informed dabbler,' the ratio of amount of time and effort required to make small advances shifts drastically, requiring hours of study and practice to achieve small 1% increments and continuing in that direction henceforth.

How do we maintain mental malleability as we age and our mind fills up with more and more data? Further complicated as we fall into routines and commitments, perhaps working at the same job for years, constantly relying upon the same skills and knowledge we've been nurturing for decades? Well, just like physical training, you've got to make yourself uncomfortable and do some heavy lifting to get those mental muscles growing. If you've been doing the exact same routine exercises at the gym for a decade, you will have plateaued about nine years ago.

Previous chapters on limitations and restrictions, as well as the preceding one focused on memory and awareness have several suggestions to increase learning and creative capacities, if need be, you can skim them for reminders, but I'll provide some additional methods in the examples below.

PLAY

Play with things and those around you, use your imagination, and dare to dream. Get down on your hands and knees and play with kids (or adults who are willing), wrestle with dogs and cats. Have fun and let your mind wander. The mind and body both undergo substantial shifts when in a state of play, of course stress will drop – you're playing and probably laughing too. Play has been shown time and again to boost creativity and learning. When having fun we're more open and responsive to both functions. In the world of physics scientists are constantly seeking a unifying theory of everything, that which allows quantum theory and relatively to co-exist, but there's another grand unifying theory I like, and it goes like this:

$$\text{PLAY} + \text{CREATIVITY} = \text{LEARNING}$$
$$\text{LEARNING} + \text{PLAY} = \text{CREATIVITY}$$
$$\text{CREATIVITY} + \text{LEARNING} = \text{PLAY}$$

All roads lead to Rome. If you can get two of the three working, the final third will fall into place.

This book provides no set definition for *play*, it's simply what works for you. For myself, the most natural thing to play is a musical instrument, something I make time for each and every day – even if only for a few minutes. This type of play allows me to drop everything, leaving both my mental and physical self focused on creation. I often work on multiple projects at once, so having an intermission and playing an instrument provides an ideal 'reset' – unless I'm working on writing songs, in which case I'd read a book or go for a walk. When creating or switching between projects, it's good to have an unrelated activity to play at allowing yourself some freedom to operate outside the space you'd previously been focused on.

MUSICAL INSTRUMENTS

Anything can be an instrument. Your voice, feet, or hands for starters – and don't say you're one of those people who 'can't sing,' the most important aspect of singing is that you believe what you're singing and sing with conviction; once you do, others will too. A quick Internet search will reveal dozens of singers and musicians and those who think 'they can't sing' or 'can't play' – but such critics miss the point, the person is expressing themselves and creating in a way they see fit, and chances are if someone out there is taking the time to write about and criticize them, many other people will listen to them because they enjoy it. In a world so large and interconnected there's an audience for anyone and anything.

Looking back to what led us here in the first place, the point is to play – cut-loose from everything else and focus your physical and mental capabilities on the instrument(s) in front of you. There's an old musician saying, "Guitar is the easiest instrument to learn but the hardest to master," and as someone who's played for over thirty years, I stand by that. If you pick up a cheap guitar or better (and cheaper) yet, a ukulele, chances are you can learn three basic chords in a week of practicing for thirty minutes a day, maybe less. Where can three basic chords take you? Again, a quick Internet search reveals dozens of videos showing how many famous songs can be played with three simple chords. This principle follows the bell curve – yes, it's unlikely that you'll be a virtuoso master of whichever instrument you choose to *play* after a few months or a year, but on the other hand you'll be competent enough to *play* what you want and improve each and every day.

COOKING & BAKING

A simple way to integrate learning and creation into your daily routine while upping your nutrition game is to start cooking and baking, or if you already do so, try some new styles, techniques, and recipes. Chefs and bakers have risen to the ranks of celebrity and rightly so; both baking and cooking are extremely creative pursuits in themselves and in hindsight, it's odd that beyond niche circles they weren't considered creative enterprises on the same level as the more 'traditional' arts. Depending on your style and what you enjoy you may be more inclined towards either baking or cooking – I find the inherent processes different, baking more akin to science and architecture, requiring specific measurements otherwise you can end up with an inedible mess, whereas cooking is fair game for pure experimentation and abstract art, a pinch of this, a splash of that, just keep tasting along the way.

OBLIQUE STRATEGIES

Musician and Producer Brian Eno worked with Berlin artist Peter Schmidt to create a set of cards known as "Oblique Strategies." Each card is printed with a phrase bearing a strange suggestion or aphorism intended for use when you hit a creative roadblock or get stuck in a rut. You pull a card (or click the app once) and follow the suggestion or go with the ideas it brings into your head as a starting point. A simple concept that can work wonders. The decks can be tricky to find and sometimes pricey, but in the true egalitarian fashion of the idea there are free versions available for both Android and iPhone.

I'm a believer in strength through adversity, and that great things are often born of accidents or out of discomfort, the entire limitations and restrictions section is based upon this ideal. What follows are two simple strategies aligning to this belief, both of which you've certainly been forced to deal with at one time or another, and may have a distaste for them; but hear me out.

DEADLINES

Who wants a deadline? How is that going to help with learning or creation? Doesn't it just create anxiety? Well, sure it might do a little bit of that but it also guarantees you will make or learn something instead of constantly putting it off until tomorrow. Remember the Silicon Valley mantra, "Done is better than perfect"? Well, that holds up and rings true. At least you'll have something from which you can begin iterating and improving upon. Getting that initial piece of work out there is the most difficult step. If you're not meeting your deadlines try making the commitments smaller rather than pushing them out.

EARLY SHOW & TELL

This is going to be uncomfortable because whatever you have *will not be up to your standards* – yet. It's a work in progress and you may not even believe in it yet. The problem with so many works in progress is that they stay just that – something you're working on, never to be completed or finished and ready to show anyone.

Two things happen when you show people something you're working on. First you'll receive feedback which will be good, bad, or middling, but that's beside the point and you can do with it what you will – shelve it, appreciate it, make changes or use negative feedback as an incentive to prove them wrong. The important thing is you've let a third-party in on something you're working on, recruiting an unsuspecting cheerleader in the process who may poke or prod you from time to time enquiring as to how your work is progressing. If months or years pass and you're still giving the same 'work-in-progress' reply, that should be a signal to shift gears and make something or make a change.

Which lead to the second benefit – you've publicly announced that you're up to something, learning or making. Now you've got outside influence and some social pressure to fuel that internal fire and get it done. And no matter how good or bad or how much of a waste of time someone views something you've done or learned, *you have done it*. You followed through on your commitment and that feels good.

COACHES, MENTORS & SUPPORTERS

Finding someone who believes in you and your work is an amazing benefit, especially when you're just starting out and don't have much to go on. Having a third-party perspective and independent set of eyes and ears can help pick you up during the inevitable times when you question what you're doing and why you're spending so much time on it. A coach, mentor, or supporter knows you well enough or has the emotional intelligence and intuition to know when you need a pick-up versus a kick in the ass. Many a great initiative has suffered due to pandering not receiving honest feedback or criticism when things weren't working.

You may have heard the line: You are the average of your five closest friends or associates. Research in social psychology shows that those you habitually associate with determine your success or failure by as much as 95%. That's a telling figure, first of all in the luck of where you're born and who you're born too, but it also could be an impetus for changes you need to make if you're having difficulty achieving your goals.

A benefit of the hyper-connected world we live in is the multiple ways you can reach out to individuals, organizations, support, and peer groups to gain valuable input and insight into your work – often free of charge. Changing your environment and those you interact with has never been easier or more available, it just takes a little effort and humility to ask for assistance.

Trusted coaches and mentors are invaluable for deepening levels of awareness, understanding your strengths and weaknesses, your approach, and your product. In some ways this echos Early Show & Tell, except a coach or mentor negates any threat of ridicule or embarrassment making it a safe avenue to gain perspective by exposing your work to trusted individuals.

The in-depth and personal feedback you receive from a tuned-in coach can set your mind and focus racing down new paths, helping you connect or see things in ways you hadn't previously. These are "Eureka!" moments, fantastic feelings resulting in flurries of work and progress making leaps and bounds towards your ultimate goals.

You may be the type that has done very well for themselves. Always in control and progressing in your life and chosen endeavours. Why would someone like that need a coach or a mentor? No matter who you are, you can always improve in certain areas, if you don't think so then you're lacking in self-awareness. Many would point to Steve Jobs, Eric Schmidt, Larry Page, and Jeff Bezos as shining examples of individuals who've done well for themselves. As such it may surprise you to discover they all had a coach, the same coach – the legendary Bill Campbell, who refused to take any salary or stock options for his services. Sadly, Mr. Campbell has since passed, but this example highlights that no matter who you are or how good you think you're doing; you too may benefit from a coach or mentor.

SUMMARY

This is the essence of everything we've ever done and will do as species or individuals. In order to survive, thrive, and culturally evolve, we need to learn and create. They are innate qualities we are born to, easily observed when watching a child at play. Unfortunately, many of the constructs and institutions we've built into our society do too good of a job of beating these instincts out of us. But we have the power to free ourselves, push back, and adopt new habits, building new connections and neural pathways in our minds. We can then continue to mold and forge our societal structures, enacting small local changes and building upon those. When done well, we thrive. Others will take notice and the ideas and concepts spread like wildfire all on their own, no marketing needed. The best thing you can do for yourself is to maintain that childlike curiosity and keep an open mind. Keep learning, keep changing and challenging your opinions, it's *not* hypocritical or wishy-washy as political attack ads may insist, it is learning and authentic growth.

Modern technology has brought us closer together – but it has a dark side in that it has resulted in a largely homogenized global culture, with few variants depending where in the world you live. From time to time it behooves us to step outside of this 'norm' to gain perspective and encourage independent, original, and unbiased thought. To do so, you need to develop some habits and techniques to allow yourself this advantage and not be absorbed and assimilated by the mass media marketed culture that surrounds us.

The advent and increase in global communications ushered this process along, snuffing out local and regionalized cultures as it spread – from automobiles, trains, and planes, to radio, television and the glory of the Internet and World Wide Web. While these changes have enabled us to share and communicate on a global level, they are not good for localized culture or independent thought. Research shows an ever-increasing rate at which languages and dialects are disappearing in the face of mass interconnectivity and communications. You may take the view that this is a natural product of our society, and that cultures come and go, rise and fall, but the speed and scale at which it's now occurring is unprecedented and it's impossible to ascertain what knowledge and wisdom is being lost to antiquity in the process.

Studies have shown that living within and experiencing different cultures enhances creativity. It's easy to see why – as we grow, learn, and experience the world around us we come to understand and define it in those terms. We develop our own vision and understanding of how the world works. When immersed in an entirely different culture new experiences begin to chip away and erode that hard-coded definition and understanding. You see and experience how things can work in alternative ways, opening and broadening your mind. The more different the culture combined with the depth of immersion (living vs. visiting), the more drastic the change. In terms of Learning & Creation, this is going all in – you'll be enveloped in new structures and experiences resulting in some discomfort, but a more than fair trade-off in the bursts of learning and creativity you receive.

EXPANDING YOUR HORIZONS

Therein is one of the greatest tragedies of cultural homogenization. In this rapidly shrinking cultural world, how do we seek out, find, explore, and immerse ourselves in truly unique and different viewpoints and ways of living? There's no easy or certain answer, and I suspect it will continue getting more difficult before it gets better, but there are a few techniques and strategies you can apply if you're the adventurous sort and willing to undergo a little discomfort. I'm lucky enough to have lived in seven countries, some being vastly different from my upbringing in Canada, some being closer to home. There are aspects of each that I adore and others I'd be very happy to never experience again; but the journey and learnings in each and every one was worthwhile and helped forge the person I am today. With that spirit of growth and adventure in mind, let's dive in:

- Take the road less traveled. Visit or move to locations that are less integrated into the modern world and off the tourist trail. Regardless of where you live there are always places of this sort, just pull up a map and take a look. Globalization hits cities and metropolitan centers first spreading out from there in ripples like those seen when dropping a pebble into a pond. As such your best bet is to target rural locations and rural adventures, where you're prone to meet and mix with people who cling to different, older values and ways of life.

- An advantage of living in this hyperconnected world is that many jobs can be performed remotely. One tangible benefit of the COVID-19 pandemic has been the increased acceptability of remote working. While the long-term effects remain to be seen, an increasing number of individuals will work remotely from far off and rural locales. If you're lucky enough to be someone who can take advantage of this situation, try living a year or two as a 'digital nomad,' taking yourself and your family anywhere you have the urge to explore.

- While the draw of large tourist attractions is understandable, it's not the best way to increase your understanding of a culture or to broaden your horizons. Well-known objects, places, and natural wonders are over-photographed and have so much written on them you can almost visit virtually without leaving the comfort of your home. Sure, it's not the same thing, but if we're focusing on culture, it's safe to say visiting something that is swarmed with tourists and marketing isn't going to awaken any latent insights inside of you anyways. Such venues are often underwhelming with much of the magic they once contained sapped away by the tourist infrastructure built around it. If need be, tick these things off your 'list' and then take advantage of the less seen and visited aspects of the area. Throw away any preconceived notions or itinerary you had in mind; ignore your guidebook and the recommendations of whichever Internet site or blog you browsed. Instead, simply walk and wander wherever your heart and curiosity takes you. If you're hungry or thirsty, choose some random local haunt where you may discover a new dish, cuisine, drink or even a friend that will stick with you for a lifetime.

- Instead of staying in fully catered accommodations such as a hotel, B&B, or hostel, try renting an apartment or a house. There's an abundance of online services enabling this sort of homestay, most offering reviews to ensure you're getting what you want and reducing risk while saving money if you're traveling on a budget. Staying in this type of accommodation will help you to feel and operate more like a local.

- A final suggestion for integrating into new cultures, regardless of how much income you may or may not have, is to volunteer or find work abroad. This is another way for you to grow, utilize your experience to chip in somewhere new; learning while also giving back and contributing to the community in which you're living.

THE ARTS

What about the other side of culture? Those we watch and listen to for entertainment and insight – I'm speaking of visual art, music, film, theatre, dance etc., commonly referred to as 'the arts.' Despite the increased availability and accessibility of these mediums, they too are in danger of homogenization.

Streaming-media algorithms are designed to force-feed you more of what you like instead of challenging your tastes and exposing you to new sights and sounds you may not have previously been aware of.

Try exploring an aspect or one of the arts you know nothing about – It's not in my nature to do this kind of thing, I the sort who believes '*I know what I like*', yet almost every single time I'm convinced to attend a theatre or dance performance I come back inspired and with my mind blown. This happens far more often than when I resort to something *I know* I enjoy, such as a concert by an artist I like or a film by a favorite director. A recent excursion to the theatre resulted in me being so smitten that I ended up attending a further six performances of the same play. Serving as the perfect example of my stubbornness – while going to see that play awakened a new understanding and appreciation of theatre, I ended up mostly stuck on the same play (though I have been to several others since!).

Despite my experience and awakening above, each and every time I am *still* reluctant to reach outside of my comfort zone and try something new. Why is this? Studies have shown we fear an unknown outcome more than known bad one. Logically, this doesn't make a lot of sense, when the unknown could result in one of the best experiences of your life versus something you know will be bad. I suspect it may have something to do with that old survival instinct, governed by the amygdala, a part of the limbic system (often referred to as the 'lizard brain'), which hasn't evolved in millennia and controls many of those powerful base emotions we struggle to overcome such as fear and anger.

If you're a maker, a person who creates things, be it writing, painting, sculpting, dancing, ceramics, music, film, or whatever medium you choose; delving into different cultural offerings, current or historical can be an amazing, relatively untapped, and endless source of inspiration. Before recorded mediums existed localized folklore, song, rhythms, dances, ceramics etc. were the primary method of passing on knowledge, warnings, morals, and values of a culture. I've been left awestruck more times than I can count in seeing or hearing something created decades or centuries ago, yet so perfectly aligned and relevant today. A close friend of mine is a lauded vinyl record collector, I can sit at his house with open ears and mind as he plays me Pakistani drumming that sounds heavier than the heaviest hip-hop beats produced today only to find they were recorded decades before anyone started rapping over looped breaks in the Bronx – the stuff is just begging to be sampled. The saying 'history repeats itself' is often true – if you want to move forward, looking back can be a good first step.

SUMMARY

We need to do everything in our power to ensure we're tolerant and open to different cultures and viewpoints. Not solely from the point of the culture or cultural aspect we're observing, but also in allowing ourselves the greatest opportunity to grow and learn and become our best selves. Being cultured isn't someone who claims to have visited x amount of countries or seen this, that, or the other thing. Culture isn't a commodity and shouldn't be treated as such. It's something to be respectfully absorbed and experienced, considered and pondered; only then can it offer up the wisdom and knowledge we desire. Don't shoehorn yourself into a readymade whistle-stop tour for the purpose of populating the social media platform of your choice. Open up and expose yourself to chance, consider what you're seeing, hearing, tasting, and touching. Delve into it and consider which aspects you could harness to enrich your life and that of those surrounding you.

We humans are simply another species of animal inhabiting and sharing this planet. Throughout history to the present day we have treated ourselves as unique and entitled, above other species on earth. We are not the center of the planet, let alone the universe; though we sit atop of the food chain as rulers of this domain, we have to ask ourselves – what kind of rulers would treat their subjects so poorly they either rise up in revolt or die off, leaving nothing left to rule?

Time is well spent alongside and observing our fellow animals, being both instructive and meditative. Watching waterfowl in a pond in springtime with young in tow can be serene. Playing with or petting a dog or a cat is a great time-out. Chance sightings of deer, foxes or other woodland animals during a hike is always a highlight. Even on screen, well produced and filmed documentaries are eye opening in the assured and innate way in which animals live and operate within the world they've evolved around.

DOMESTICATED BEST FRIENDS

Domestic animals have co-evolved alongside us for so long that they have become very attuned to human emotion and behavior. They know and understand us in unique and non-judgmental ways, it's easy to understand why people and their pets get so attached. Studies show real physical and mental benefits gained by spending time with animals:

- Reduced risk of depression and anxiety.

- Lower blood pressure and stress levels.

- Playing with animals elevates levels of serotonin and dopamine, helping you calm down and relax.

- Adding structure to your day via feeding, walking, companionship etc. It's reassuring to have something you can always rely on.

- Vitality – Animals like to play, and play is good for both relaxation and ideation. They do things that seem silly and crazy, making us laugh. Certain animals require a good amount of outdoor exercise. All of which boost your immune system, mood, and energy levels.

- Provide a variety of benefits for old and young alike, from companionship in old age, reducing loneliness and fostering a sense of purpose. Animals can help young children learn empathize and relate, building a solid base for future human relationships. Pets are trusted companions of children and unlike most adults surrounding them, they never give orders or tell them to do things, it's pure play and bonding.

Several organizations harness the benefits above in the form of therapies; ranging from animals visiting retirement and assisted living facilities to increase the mood of residents, to helping children with attention or hyperactivity disorders, or people dealing with anger and aggression issues.

LESSONS FROM FELLOW SPECIES

There's a longstanding debate as to what separates humans from other animal species – exactly why and how did we rise to prominence? Rather than throw my hat into the ring in effort to settle that argument, I'll do what we often try to avoid, and generalize.

Non-human animals tend to experience life and the world around them through perceptual sensation and intuitive interaction with the environment. The conceptual world is less likely to enter into the equation, certain exclusions notwithstanding, animals do not plan or conceive of actions or concepts, they simply do – based on instinct and their sensual perception. In such, perhaps exhibiting the purest form of savage disciplines.

Consider how much we can learn from watching other species live and experience reality in this natural form. Looking back to the chapter on memory and awareness, how rare it is to find a human with anything close to the level of situational awareness of a wild animal?

Animal reliance on instinct and perceiving senses is exponential compared to humans. We can learn a lot about awareness and perception by observing different species of animals in different environments and situations.

Most days I sit in a park near my house in front of a pond filled with ducks, swans and other waterfowl. Many pigeons come by hoping to snatch food and leftovers from people feeding the other birds. If you live in a city chances are you see a lot of pigeons too – take a moment to watch them, observing their feet and talons. You'll notice it's quite rare to find pigeons with undamaged feet. Many are missing a number of talons and it's not unusual to spot several with only a stump remaining. I'm uncertain as to the cause of the pigeons' massacred feet, but have little doubt cohabiting with humans plays a role. It's possible that the talons get caught-up in strings, wires, and such, and when they break free they lose a foot or talon in the process.

Not a pleasant image but if you look beyond the nastiness, take a moment to admire the sheer *perseverance* of the pigeon. A common trait amongst wild animals, I venture the force of will to survive in the face of any adversity, disability, limitation, restriction, and to push through pain is unparalleled in humanity. I've observed this perseverance and capacity to push aside pain and persist again and again in other animal species and it continues to astound me.

It's worth mentioning how non-human members of the animal kingdom manage to live sustainably with nature and to adapt better than us. Something worth reflecting upon.

SUMMARY

We are animals. We just happen to be the species that's strayed furthest from its wild and natural roots to both good and bad effect. The majority of us exist so far afield from the way of life which gave us rise that our minds and bodies are in constant states of agitation and aggravation, fighting to function as they were designed to do over millennia of evolution. As a result, it's not only soothing but beneficial to ourselves and the world surrounding us to step down from our ruler's pedestal and immerse ourselves in the natural world from which we came, spending time with, observing, and learning from our fellow species.

CHAPTER FIFTEEN

ADVENTURE & RISK TAKING

"Fortune favors the bold," an quote attributed to both Virgil (poet and author of the Aeneid, as well as Dante's guide in the Divine Comedy) and Alexander the Great. You need not conquer nations and build an enormous empire, nor descend into the nine circles of hell; but stepping outside your comfort zone and surprising yourself is an understated tool that everyone should have in their arsenal. Similar in spirit to mediation, it's a constant practice and process of starting from a blank slate and reassessing yourself each and every time, with this in mind I've labeled this 'Adventure Practice.'

You may think that some individuals naturally have a higher risk tolerance, are braver, or born adventurers, and this may be true but only to a point. Like all aspects of life certain individuals are predisposed to a higher competency in some things and lower in others. Jumping out of an airplane may not be a big deal for one person, particularly after completing dozens of jumps; but the thought of entering a math competition or singing in public terrifies them. Something that is easy for you may be extremely difficult for someone else and vice versa. That's part of what adventure and risk taking is – confronting your fears and weaknesses head-on, knowing you may fail or make a fool of yourself, only to find that both are really no big deal, you'll get over it and live to fight another day. With that in hindsight, something that may have felt uncomfortable or given you pause in the past can instead be empowering, building resilience and courage for future endeavours.

HOW TO ADVENTURE

Adventures can be as big or small as you want them to be. With that in mind, I encourage you to have some form of adventure whenever possible. Walk a new and random route around your city or neighborhood. Order something different at a frequented restaurant or cafe. Read a book on a subject or by an author you've never heard of. Listen to only new and unknown music, not in your playlists or auto-suggested selections for an entire week.

The boost and benefits you get from stepping outside your comfort zone, challenging yourself, and surmounting those challenges is huge. I've no doubt this is what gives birth to "adrenaline junkies" – the term given to folks who live for exactly this kind of rush.

A few of benefits you can expect your mind and body to enjoy:

- Resilience – Both physical and mental. Chances are you're going to put either or both to the test. You're going to come across some form of adversity and force yourself to adapt to overcome it. You'll remember this for the next time and onwards down the line, continually building your resilience.

- Bonding – Nothing builds a sense of togetherness and knits a group together like being placed in a tight spot and having to cooperate to resolve the situation. The friendships I've made while working in the war-ravaged environments of the Balkans and Afghanistan will always remain close due to sense of trust developed while there. I have similar feelings towards those who I've embarked on large off-grid adventures with. There's a reason many team building programs and exercises are built around challenges or adventures, because it works.

- Focus – When you step outside your comfort zone or place yourself in an unfamiliar environment or situation, that amygdala brain kicks in heightening your focus and awareness. You're venturing into the unknown and your mind and body will be on high alert, ensuring they're protected. You'll enter 'the zone,' focused on exactly where you are and what you're doing, a good practice for anything in life.

- Stress Reduction & Sleep – A lot of adventuring takes place outdoors where you'll benefit from fresh air and negative ionization. You're focused, forced to act and make decisions on the spot – a habit you can learn from and nurture. Instead of worrying and stressing over situations, you think of ways to resolve and deal with them. All of the above, fresh air, negative ions, exercise, and reduced stress will result in a better night's sleep, ensuring your mind and body have the full opportunity to recover.

- Confidence & Drive – Achievement works wonders. When you surprise yourself in what you can accomplish this turns into increased confidence and drive. You've just completed something you previously thought you couldn't do – why not push forward with a new and different challenge now that you've surmounted that mental roadblock?

- Gratitude & Perspective – This is a big one for me. In such a complex and overcrowded world it's easy to lose perspective, get frustrated and angry with injustices or things that aren't going your way. As you explore you're certain to come across people and situations that cause you to reflect and see things differently – calling into question how bad things really are or as is often the case, aren't. Despite how hard-done-by you feel, when you come across entire societies who are very happy living with much less it gives you pause for thought. It doesn't mean you should be complacent but you may feel more gracious for what you have and approach your solutions (and frustrations) with a fresh perspective.

- Exploration – You will actually get to see new places and things, some of which are only accessible via trekking, climbing, kayaking, diving, off-roading etc. In the Culture chapter, we refer to those overrun must-see tourist traps, adventuring gives you an opportunity to make your own personalized list of 'must sees', special ones requiring a little more effort than buying a ticket and waiting in line. That extra effort will give those experiences much more meaning to you and you'll have a greater chance of retaining those feelings and memories.

- Increased Energy – I've lost count of how many times I've returned home from business trips or vacations and needed to take an extra day to recover. Instead of feeling rested and relaxed I was stressed. When you return from an adventure (be it a vacation, a weekend, or day long excursion), you'll feel energized and full of endorphins, ready and raring to go, push forward and surmount the next challenge.

- Stories & Learning – No one likes going through another person's vacation photos and to that point, I recommend keeping picture-taking to a minimum. You will remember the experience more if you engage and immerse yourself directly, not via a lens or a screen. However, everyone loves being pulled into engaging and harrowing tales of a crazy adventures – the things they saw, how they dealt with such-and-such a situation etc. You'll have stories to tell, which will make you a better storyteller, and both yourself and others will learn from your experiences.

SUMMARY

There's no reason you can't make adventuring part of your everyday life via a series of 'mini-adventures.' A mini-adventure is simply something to break up a habit or routine you've developed. Even changing the order in which you do something will require you to focus and concentrate in a new way, and you may surprise yourself in finding that new method works better than the previous one.

Several years back, London experienced a strike of its underground train system (subway, tube etc.), as a result commuters had to develop alternate ways to get to and from work.

Surprisingly, when the strike ended a large percentage of individuals stuck to the new routes they'd been forced to discover, finding they worked better or preferred them.

Adventuring and taking risks builds character, develops new skills, strengthens resilience, increases focus and broadens your perspective. You'll become more familiar with yourself, your capabilities, and your limits. When you push yourself both mentally and physically you'll note how the stress and chaos of everyday life seems to fade away, softening into a muted background buzz.

Developing and maintaining these habits takes work and effort. It's easy to get comfortable, fall into routine and rigid mindsets, closing ourselves off to the world and retreating into the hubbub of our daily grind; immersed in our work and social lives. Keeping alert and forcing oneself to step outside of routine in an attempt to stay fresh, dynamic and adapting is a skill which must be honed and practiced like any other, but one that's well worth the effort.

Time to put this to bed. Everything you've worked for, the new habits you've developed, structures and strategies you've put into place to ensure you're operating at your best, this is when you lay them to rest. And you need to, because sleep is the final leg of that three-legged stool upon which everything stands; Bad sleep habits can tip the entire thing over, making it all for naught.

Rumor has it that Albert Einstein slept around 10-hours a night, on top of which he would take several naps during the day. Someone who practices that kind of sleep schedule today is likely be called out for sloth, but not many berate Einstein for laziness or lack of productivity. Based on the above example, Einstein preferred a long, uninterrupted period of monophasic sleep, followed by several micro-naps, culminating in a polyphasic day.

Other historically productive individuals such as Leonardo Da Vinci, Nikola Tesla, and Thomas Edison, famously employed polyphasic sleep patterns. Instead of sleeping flat out for a 7+ hour period each night, they would indulge in smaller portions of sleep every 4 hours or so. Despite how odd this may sound to many of us, most mammals operate on polyphasic sleep patterns, which you're sure to have noticed if you've ever owned or been around a dog or a cat.

Biphasic sleep is common practice in many parts of the world which employ traditions of afternoon siestas or naps, usually between lunch and dinner.

It's estimated that humans sleep a full hour less than we did before the invention of the electric light. Research has turned up an entirely separate stage of our circadian rhythms (sleep cycle) when humans used to rise and sleep with the sun, a state known as "the watch."

How you sleep matters less than ensuring you get the proper amount of sleep for your mind and body to recover and function. If you find you can't sleep more than 4-5 hours at a stretch this may be your body telling you that you're inclined towards a biphasic or polyphasic sleep pattern, and you should begin incorporating naps into your daily routine. Experiment with different methods of sleep to see what makes you feel and perform your best.

For most of us, changing our sleep pattern is not a trivial or easy task, particularly when juggling other commitments such as family or a demanding career. It will require determination and creativity, perhaps even a professional medical assessment. But isn't a little hassle worth the effort if it makes you feel and perform that much better on a daily basis?

BEFORE BED

Limit your caffeine intake, particularly in the ±8 hours leading up to your sleep. While we're on the subject, try not to drink *anything* at least an hour before bed, water included, which is liable to make you get up and use the bathroom, interrupting your sleep.

You also don't want to eat a large meal any less than 2-3 hours before sleep, as your stomach will be churning and digesting when you get into bed, and that definitely won't help your sleep. If you do eat something make it light and easily digestible, and preferably without sugar.

Alcohol is one of the worst culprits for inhibiting sleep. There are mountains of evidence supporting this, and if you happen to have one of those sleep tracking devices, it's a simple experiment to perform yourself. Track your sleep on a night when you've had no alcohol whatsoever, and again when you've had a single glass of wine. The difference is alarming.

If you can get outside during the day, do so. Fresh air and negative ions are great for clearing your mind and calming you down, encouraging a healthy sleep. In many cultures it's customary to go for an after-dinner walk, this is a great option – it gets you outside and moving, helping both digestion and to prepare you for a good night of rest. Recent trends towards television or movies after dinner aren't near as conducive towards a good sleep.

Get in the habit of going over your schedule for the following day sometime between dinner and bedtime. When I go to bed, I know what 85% of my next day is going to look like. Not only does this help settle your mind, but it'll also ensure you're prepared for the day.

The last thing I do in the evening and first thing I do in the morning are the same – I read. Similar to walking, it's a good way to close the day, relax your mind and focus your attention on a single item, perhaps even something you want your subconscious to mull over while sleeping. An item of note here, if you're reading on a device or by a light, ensure it's soft and preferably blue light filtered.

Speaking of blue light, most electronic devices emit this frequency which emulates daylights and signals our brains to wake-up. Many device manufacturers or third parties have gotten wise to this, providing filters and options to remove the blue light frequency from your device (my phone does this automatically, attuned to sunrise and sunset). Check for such settings or blue-light blockers for your devices. I'd recommend not using electronics in the last hour or two before bed, but if you must, make sure they're not emitting blue light and messing with your sleep.

I live in London, England, which is pretty far north if you look at a map. In the summer months we have very long days, the sun rising extremely early in the morning and setting late in the evening. Light wakes me up more than sound, so to ensure I have cozy darkness to encourage a full night's sleep I wear a sleep mask – those silly things you see in sitcoms and cartoons that folks wear on airplanes. You need to make your bedroom a 'sleep chamber,' as comfortable and conducive to sleep as possible. Make it dark, use a mask, or black-out curtains or blinds. Make it the goldilocks temperature for you, not too hot, not too cold.

JET LAG

An ailment which assails us in the modern age is brought on by the low-cost convenience of high-speed travel on jet aircraft.

Jet lag, otherwise known as desynchronosis or flight fatigue, is something many of us have experienced at one point or another, and some battle on a regular basis. During different phases of my life, I've slotted into the latter category, hopping timezones far too often to be healthy. As such, I've developed certain methods to combat this nemesis and shake off any lingering fatigue or insomnia in short order. Just like hangovers, there is no 'miracle cure.' What works for me may need to be adapted for you.

1. Minimize alcohol and caffeine during your flight. Avoid it if possible, but if not, try to limit yourself to no more than 1-2 servings of each.

2. Participate in some form of physical exercise every day, at least for the first 3-4 days, really get your heart rate up and break a sweat. Don't hurt yourself and vary the type of activity, if necessary.

3. Again, post-flight, for the first few days restrict your alcohol and caffeine consumption, refraining if possible. I understand this may be difficult, but it makes a huge difference.

4. At the earliest opportunity post-arrival, force yourself into the daily rhythm of your destination. For most of us, this means rising sometime between 5-8am and going to sleep between 9pm-12am

5. *[Optional]* Melatonin drops/spray/pills. Melatonin is a natural hormone your body produces when it's time for you to sleep – it is not artificial, chemically assisted sleep. I find this helps for long jumps, anything greater than 8 hours of time

difference. For the first 3-4 days, I'll take a dose 30 minutes before bed, gradually reducing the dosage each day. Medical professionals I've spoken with have informed me it works for some people and not others, but if you're planning a long-haul journey and have had difficulty acclimating to time shifts in the past, it's an inexpensive option worth trying.

SUMMARY

Getting enough sleep matters; it's a core pillar of health and wellbeing. The amount of rest you give your mind and body will affect each and every thing you do for better or worse. *How* you sleep, be it a long uninterrupted stretch or several smaller stretches throughout the day, matters much less than ensuring you get enough to function at your best. There is no sleep credit or debit system, you can't get 12-hours one day and exchange it for 4-hours the next – our circadian rhythms have evolved around the 24-hour cycle of an Earth day and that balance resets each and every day.

The quality of your sleep is of equal importance. Sleep assisted by chemicals or drugs, i.e. sleeping pills, is not a good option. I have taken sleeping pills once in my life, and I don't think I've experienced a more difficult wake-up or groggy day since. It was not a good experience and most medical professionals agree that chemically assisted sleep should *only* be used as a last resort, and even then, you should keep searching for natural solutions.

Congratulations on making it to the end. I hope the contents contained herein have provided you with ample amounts of value and insight. As mentioned at the start, pick and choose what works for you – we're all different, and we need to tweak and nudge ourselves in different ways to be our best. Although everyone's formula is bespoke, most techniques discussed in this book look back hundreds or thousands of years and we have evolved to operate within those parameters. As such, they can be applied universally, you simply need to determine how to best adjust and fit them into your life.

Do I do each and every single thing written in this book all of the time? Of course not, I'm human and I fail a lot. In fact, because I'm inclined towards experimentation, I often change things up, trying new approaches only to discover it doesn't work for me or I'm simply not good at it. That aside, I am pretty consistent and dedicated, and estimate I do everything written in this book, every day, more than 90% of the time. You can check in with anyone who knows me to confirm that.

History shows that 80% is a pretty good marker or level setter – getting you an 'A' in school, putting you at the top of the class and allowing for a much deserved day of rest too. Use these methods and techniques to develop a framework to be your best self, to get things done and perform and the best you can. If you set a target to stick to the routine 80% of the time, I guarantee you'll notice a huge difference, not only in how you feel, but in your overall quality of life. Have fun with it and treat yourself with respect. Be disciplined and hold yourself to a high standard. You only live once and for a very brief period, the journey should be enjoyable.